THE 12-MINUTE MBA

FOR DOCTORS

By Charles Johnson With Andy Thibault

MICHELLE PUBLISHING COMPANY
ROCKY HILL, CT 06067

Johnson, Charles, 1948 -

The 12-Minute MBA for Doctors

Copyright © 2001 by Charles Johnson

Published by Michelle Publishing Company, Rocky Hill, CT.

ISBN 0-9626001-2-1

Table of Contents

Preface

by Joseph F. Bentivegna M.D.

Medicine is the only profession where increased productivity is penalized with less respect and lower incomes. Sound ridiculous? Well let's look at the facts. In the 1950s, medicine was in the Stone Age. Myocardial infarctions were treated with digoxin, morphine, bed rest and holy water. Kidney stones and gallstones were removed after filleting the abdomen. Cataract surgery was done by making huge incisions that traversed half the cornea. The patients lay in bed for weeks with sandbags surrounding their heads. Afterwards, they had to wear thick glasses that distorted their vision. Many felt they were better off prior to the surgery.

Fast forward to the new millennium. Myocardial infarctions are attacked with angioplasties, bypasses and an array of highly specific medications. Kidney stones are destroyed with ultrasonic waves that obviate the need for surgery. Gallstones can be removed with micro-abdominal incisions that result in patient recovery in days. Cataract surgery is now a twelve-minute operation done with topical anesthesia. Many

1

patients are driving the next day with uncorrected (no glasses) 20/20 vision!

One would expect that doctors, who go to school and train for endless hours would be rewarded, both financially and socially, for these spectacular advances. What has actually happened is the opposite. Doctors have seen their incomes drop (after adjusting for inflation) since the 1950s. In fact, it is not unusual for doctors to make less money than the drug sales people who are constantly traipsing into their offices!

Doctors are no longer even called "doctors," but rather "health care providers!" They retain all liability for poor results while faceless government and insurance company bureaucrats call the shots.

Patients are frustrated too. They used to be able to go to a doctor's office and have their problems solved. Now they are bounced around from pharmacies to laboratories to X-ray departments. After enduring all this hassle, they have to spend hours on hold with some insurance company just to get reimbursed. No wonder patients are embracing alternative medicine and blowing money on useless herbs promoted by modern-day shamans.

How did this mess evolve?

It is because doctors refuse to play the game. Doctors assume that if they play by the rules, everything will be fine. What they don't understand is that the rules are constantly changing, and they have no input.

Enter Charlie Johnson.

Charlie worked for United States Surgical Corporation where he was responsible for creating over twenty partnerships with academic medical centers. During this time, he realized that most practicing physicians today have little business training. He understands the skills that are required for survival in our increasingly media-savvy and market-oriented society. If doctors want to protect their profession and their patients, it is not enough to simply be competent. They must learn the same skills Charlie has mastered—leadership, persuasive communication, conflict resolution, tactical planning and management.

All physicians must read this book. Not only will they then understand what it takes to survive in today's culture, they will learn how to be active participants. They will learn to play the game

Dr. Bentivegna is an ophthalmologist in Rocky Hill, Connecticut. He has authored numerous articles on health care and was a candidate for the U.S. Senate in 1994. He is the author of *The Neglected and Abused: A Physician's Year in Haiti,* now in its fourth printing. His first novel, *The Lords of Greenwich,* will be published shortly.

Introduction

Surgeons are still trained like blacksmiths. Although they are at the pinnacle of their profession, they tend to know little about business—how to negotiate a lease, hire staff or negotiate with an insurance company.

I learned this working with surgeons and other medical professionals throughout the United States during the last 20 years. A couple of years ago, after delivering a 12-minute talk before the Society for University Surgeons in New Orleans, several colleagues asked me for help running their businesses. One of them advised me to call my program, "The 12-Minute MBA For Doctors."

This made a lot of sense to me. Many of the professions have little or no formal business training. Doctors and lawyers, for example, tend not to study

practical business skills such as persuasive communication, team building and conflict resolution. It is
assumed they have developed these skills through life
experience, on the job or from a mentor.

Our system of surgical residency was created in the
early 1900s. Dr. William Halsted of Johns Hopkins
University took medical school graduates and basically
put them in apprenticeships for five years.

Today, surgeons stand side-by-side with a mentor
who shows them what to do, lets them try, stops them
when they begin to get into trouble, or stops them
when they fail. The primary tool of training is
observation and criticism. It's the way you teach a
tradesman.

A few years ago there were about 35 openings for
surgery department chairs out of about 135 major
university programs in the U.S. Nobody wants the job.
A person goes from having a busy surgical practice to
becoming an administrator. He becomes responsible for
balancing budgets, generating revenue streams, strategic planning and implementation, hiring and firing,
resolving conflict, building high-performing teams,
negotiations—all within the context of a health system
that is suffering from diminishing revenues and expanding challenges.

Health care is run more and more by business
people—not doctors. Hospital administrators tend to be
business people. Insurance companies have everything
to do with the running of health care today. The
physician now has to deal on an everyday basis with
business people.

Look at the history of these very bright people:
They go through four years of college, four years of
medical school and then five years or more of residency
and fellowship education—all of that time earning no

5

more than probably $35,000 a year. When they finally complete their training in their early to mid-30s, the first thing they have to do is go out into a world that is run by business. It's not run by their peers.

So how does a 32-year-old who just completed a residency negotiate a contract—a contract with an employer or even a contract with a landlord? How does he strategically plan his business? How does he persuade people to come to work for him? How does he interview people? How does he really get his business started?

I offer the answers in this book. Some chapters might take more than 12 minutes to read and digest, but many readers tell us they benefit significantly from any 12-minute helping.

Starting a practice means renting office space, hiring help, going out and attracting patients through referrals or persuading the primary care physicians in your marketplace to send their patients your way. You have to negotiate contracts with insurance providers, and you have to have a business plan that allows you to build a successful business.

There's not one place in those four years of college or four years of medical school or five years of residency or a year or two more of fellowship that teaches you one thing about business. There's no business course at all.

Academics know these skills need to be taught, but there's no time. Do you take a person out of a surgical rotation to attend a course on negotiation? Sure, they want to do that, but they choose not to interfere with the important medical education. People understand the importance of business training, but it's not urgent, so very little has been done.

I would like to create an opportunity for every

physician, either in academics or in private practice, to learn practical business skills. In this book, I have identified what I consider the eight practical business skills necessary for success. The first is persuasive communication skills. Other elements of the program include leadership skills, team building, conflict resolution, knowledge of financial strategies and strategic and tactical planning skills, as well as negotiation and interviewing and hiring skills.

If you have time, go ahead and take a year or two off and get that MBA. Or, if you want to start taking control of your business right away, just turn the page.

Charles Johnson
Andy Thibault
Litchfield, Connecticut, August 17, 2001

Chapter 1

PERSUASIVE COMMUNICATION

When I talk with physicians about persuasive communication, some have said, "Oh my God, don't try to turn me into a salesman." All those skills seem so abhorrent to them.

Persuasive communication is really something more basic than sales. You use it every day of your life. Here are just a few examples:

- You wake up in the morning and you want to persuade your teenage son to take out the trash or turn down the stereo or get up for school.

- You need to persuade your spouse to go to the bank and pick up the dry cleaning, get the car washed or fill up the gas tank.

- You need to convince your secretary to work overtime to finish a project.

- You need to convince a device manufacturer to support an upcoming program.

- You want to convince your superior to fund a project.

- You need to persuade a materials manager to buy a new product you need.

- You need to get the scheduling secretary to give you desired time in the operating room schedule.

- You need to solicit a patient to enter a randomized trial.

- You want to convince a top resident to join your practice.

- You need to convince your colleagues to support your ideas.

- You need to convince a physician to refer patients to you.

All of these are opportunities to use persuasive communication skills to achieve your objectives. That's the difference between persuasive communication and pure selling skills. You're not trying to sell a product to someone; you're trying to get someone to agree to give something so you can achieve your objectives.

If the physician is the boss, why does she need these skills?

Many times within medical organizations, people have position power. That means they have the ability to mandate that people do things.

What we're talking about is people or persuasive power; the ability to convince people to do things that you want them to do and demonstrate that you will both win.

This is not rocket science or molecular biology. As the author Steven Covey said, "this is common sense but not common practice." It's a simple understanding of people.

How does persuasive communication work? I break it down into simple steps:

• **In order to convince or persuade someone to do something, the first thing you need to do is provide them with your full attention, and in turn, get their full attention.** It's very difficult to get someone to listen to you if you look like you're busy or only giving them half an ear. So you need to create an environment of enthusiasm. You need to look happy, smile and look at your prospect as an opportunity. You need to create an environment where people will be willing to give you the information you need to be successful. Again, this is common sense but not common practice.

• **Identify the other person's needs.** You need to find out what the other person needs first. To do this, you need to ask open-ended questions, questions that beg for an elaborate answer. The best way is to say, "Joe, tell me about your experiences in writing articles for magazines" or "tell me about your experiences as a baseball coach." Just use the words, "tell me about," or "tell me more about," or "I'm curious about something." You are asking for some background information in whatever you want to find out about. People say that makes sense. It's not high-level science. It's understanding that there are systems you can use to apply common sense and achieve your objectives.

Say you are a colleague and I want to convince you to support something I'm doing. I might say to you, "Tell me about the important projects you're working on." Or, I might want to find out what's important to you. I might say, "What's important to you in your academic career? What's important to you in your practice? What's important to you in your family?"

• **"What's Important To You" and "Tell Me About" are two great ways to get people to talk about a topic.** Two things are happening when you ask these questions:

> • You're demonstrating an interest in that person.

> • You're getting their attention. You're making them speak to you before you speak to them. One thing is universal to all human beings: The most important person to anyone is herself. And people love to talk about themselves.

While people are telling you all these wonderful things about their important projects or their important interests or their academic career or their professional practice, what you need to do is to actively listen. Active listening is a skill that takes practice.

Most of us, particularly around the house, know we are not the best listeners. Active listening can be accomplished by doing a couple of things: You have to look at the person talking—you have to look at that person and demonstrate and use all of your senses—not just your ears, use your eyes to see his body language and his emotion. Use your feelings to feel how excited he may be about something. Use all of the senses to really engage yourself in that person for that period of time. While you're listening you want to make mental notes or written notes. There's nothing wrong with jotting down a note or two about something interesting the person has just talked to you about. Because by making mental or written notes, now you have something to refer back to when it's your turn to speak.

If you've done a good job listening to his wants and needs, what you're going to begin doing is aligning his wants and needs to your needs. If you tell me one of the things that is very important to you is your interest in baseball and that comes out with a lot of enthusiasm, then I can correlate your baseball interest to my interest in my project. Now we're going to start to get a connection. You can't be crazy and take leaps that are too far apart because people will think you are trying to manipulate them. But if you listen carefully to people, particularly if they are telling you what is important to them about their life or their career, you are going to find a lot of things in common with what you have. That's the beauty of the process.

Now you're beginning to match their needs and wants to the activity you want them to perform. You need to identify how your wishes help them achieve their goals. For example, suppose I was talking to a prospective secretary and I said, "What's important to you?"

She responded, "Well, what's important to me is I'm a single parent, I want to be at home for my kid on important days. I need to be available to answer the phone in case there's a problem at school. I need to feel comfortable that my child is safe and that I can be available for him."

I can link the job to those needs and say, "I need somebody who really cares about things like that, about her children, about being available on an as-needed basis for those situations. And in fact, I think that would be perfectly fine if you needed to be home if the child is sick. Maybe we can work out a way where you can work at home on those particular days." Ultimately, if you begin to give of yourself before you ask the other person for a favor, you are matching that person's needs and wants to the activity that you want.

We've linked your needs and wants with my goals and objectives, or the activity I'd like you to perform. I now need to be able to say to you—in sales we call this a trial close—"Joe, can you see how performing this task will help you achieve your objectives with the youth baseball program?" If you say "Yes, OK," then we agree to do it. Now you might say "No." No is an objection. It's very important. Many people, in trying to persuade others, try to avoid objections because they don't want to have to deal with them. But really, the objection is the most important thing you can uncover. Because when a person says "No," now you ask him, "Why?"

Hopefully, he'll state an objection. The objection might be as simple as "I don't have time that day. But I can do it another day." So you go on. Or, "I don't want to do that because it offends me," or "I don't feel I have the skill sets to do it" or "I don't want to do that task because it's going to take too much time."

Once I identify the objection, I can deal with either trying to overcome it or realize that I'm expecting too much and come back with another consideration. "OK, if you can't give me eight hours on this project, could you give me four hours or two hours?" At some point, by identifying the objection, I can start to overcome it by finding a way to have the benefit for you equal the work I am asking you to do.

In sales we look at that as a price-to-benefit ratio. There's a benefit to you for buying my product, but maybe the benefit to you is worth $10 and my product is $20. Either I have to improve the benefit to you to reach that $20 level, or drop my price to what you see as fair. It's really a give and take, and that's all persuasive communication is.

Assuming we get over the objection and we find a middle ground—a compromise—we find something that you win by doing it and I win by you doing it, and you get something and I get something. Now we agree to a plan.

A win-win plan needs a couple of things. It needs a stated set of expected behaviors or actions that each party is going to take. What's really important is, when you've persuaded someone to do something—by identifying their needs, matching them with your wants, overcoming their objections and coming up with a plan—you need to now identify and define the objectives of that plan and write them down. That way, you'll forever have a record of what you both agreed to do.

To me, that's persuasive communication. It's really not that difficult. I don't think it takes a lot of scientific understanding, but it does take practice. You can't just say "OK, now I know the steps of a persuasive communication event," and go out and do it. You need to practice it. The place I think people should practice it is at home. Imagine the startling benefits when you create a positive environment for communicating with your significant other and with your kids. Imagine the possibilities when you ask them what's important to them or ask them to tell you about their day or to give you some examples of what's been rewarding in their activities. Imagine asking them to do something and linking their needs and wants with what you want them to do. And if they say "No," instead of getting angry, asking them "Why?" And eventually you will come to a plan.

One of the stories I like to use to illustrate this involves a presentation to a group of sales people. I talked about how, on a normal day, you go home from your job and what are the first three answers you hear from your significant other: for most people it's three words—fine, fine, chicken.

Why is that? Simple. The questions you asked when you first came in the door were probably: "How was your day? How are the kids? What's for dinner?"

You've asked three very closed probes. You haven't created any opportunity for great conversation. You haven't created any good opportunity to catch great information that will help you later. Next time try this: "Tell me about your day." This question allows your significant other to elaborate on the day, both the good and the bad.

After I spent a day with one of my sales managers, I was invited to his house for dinner. We talked about a strategy before we went to his home. I said, "Let's try it." We walked in the door and he said "hello" to his wife. He then said, "Tell me about your day." She started to say, "Fine," but then she heard his question. "Well, the kids and I went shopping and we went to the park and we played on the swing, and ... " At the end of the dinner, when he drove me to my hotel, he said it was just amazing how much different that greeting was and how much more information he had. He could actually hear information she was imparting and give her positive feedback. It really set up a good evening.

In almost every communication transaction you are trying to persuade people with your people power instead of your position power. The only people who will respond to your position power are your subordinates or your kids—sometimes. Mastering the skills of persuasive communication will be highly beneficial in getting others to perform activities that will help you achieve your goals. How about your employees? Do the people in your office who have high customer contact also have persuasive communication skills?

If I want to communicate a very important item to you, and I want to persuade you, the best environment for me to do that is in my office, not your office. I want to get you—the prospect—into a place where you're not distracted by your telephone or the picture on the wall or any of your own "stuff," your secretary or your personal issues—things that are always a priority when people are in their own offices. This is why the boss usually brings you to her office to convince you to fulfill a certain task or follow a certain course. When the communication occurs in someone's home space, the authority is clear: "This is my office and you will follow my plan." Someone's office is a very tough place to get his undivided attention. You can tell your secretary to hold calls or not interrupt, but you can't tell someone else's secretary to do the same when you are visiting.

If I'm the chairman of the department of surgery or

medicine, and I want to convince one of my subordinates to work on a particular project with me, I want to create an undisturbed environment in which we can communicate well. The best place to do that is my place; he's there to meet with me, he's not distracted, and the position of control, because it is my space, rests with me. Or we could meet in a neutral spot where we're both on equal ground, such as the cafeteria, where neither one of us has the power or protection of our own environment.

Public environments are difficult if the issues are of a potentially private or personal nature, but they certainly are neutral and put both parties on an equal level.

Certainly the weakest place to persuade someone is in her office or space, yet we are continually confronted with the issue, particularly if you are the subordinate trying to persuade the boss. It may be difficult to get the boss to your office or space to make your presentation. Let's face it—if you can only persuade someone in your own space, you may never get the chance. Therefore, it becomes very important that you become able to get the attention of your prospect in spite of the location.

The key to success in persuading someone else is to get her undivided attention. If you don't have it, you cannot possibly get her to consider new ideas or a change in activity or behavior.

Remember, we talked about getting the prospect to remark on something that is meaningful in his life? You can identify clues by quickly scanning his office. The benefits of commenting on something important to that person can be enormous. There is a subconscious link between that good memory and you who brought it up in the first place. Once your prospect is talking, he is revealing to you some of the things that are most important to him. If you can eventually link those important things to the ideas you are trying to convey, you are on your way to persuading that person to help you achieve your goals. The idea is to create an environment where you will get the prospect (persuadee) to pay attention to your communication.

The Eight Steps of a Persuasive Communication are:

1. Create the appropriate environment.
2. Ask open-ended questions.
3. Identify the other person's needs.
4. Match that person's needs to your activity.
5. Ask for support.
6. Identify and overcome objections.
7. Gain each party's commitment.
8. Create and write an action plan.

Persuading someone to do something that benefits that person in the long run is a really great service. If you look at the art of persuasion as a process of helping someone else solve a problem or fulfill a need while they are actually helping you, it is a truly a win-win. I can tell you that having a skilled salesperson ask me the important questions about my needs, wants and desires, and then demonstrating how her product or service fulfills those needs, wants, and desires is something I actually appreciate.

Walking into an automobile showroom to look at a car means I have already established a need, or I wouldn't be there. Having an insurance salesperson get me to look at my insurance needs, which I haven't looked at for five or more years, is helping me to focus on an important but easy-to-overlook area in my life.

Of course, we are all annoyed by the constant barrage of salespeople trying to sell us cheaper phone service or security systems for our homes. The best persuaders, on the other hand, are actually helping their prospects or customers fulfill needs.

Persuasive communication provides the mutual gain of both parties having their needs fulfilled.

Chapter 2

LEADERSHIP

The term leadership certainly is used more than it is understood. But if you look into the world and literature of medicine today, leadership is precisely what is needed.

This is not management, this is leading people. Management is the act of directing others what to do. It's really position power: "I can manage you because I have authority over you in the existing organizational structure."

Leadership, on the other hand, is the ability to identify and articulate a vision. It is the ability to empower individuals to have ownership in a plan—facilitating them to take action to fulfill an organization's goals.

Leaders have satisfied employees; they do not have high turnover. The employees feel they are a part of the solution rather then a part of the problem. As a leader, you are actually organizing people and moving them in a certain direction, but allowing them to use their own energy and their own ideas and their own thoughts.

If you go to *Webster's Dictionary* and look up the

word "manage," its definition has to do with controlling a horse. To "lead" means you're going with, or in front of, a person or group, through some new challenge.

If you know how to lead in today's climate, you establish a milieu of collegiality and individual ownership in the organization's plan. From bank presidents to the heads of surgery departments, consensus has been building that this is the right and most effective path.

The sage of management, Peter Drucker, talks about leadership in a *Forbes* magazine article entitled, "Everything You Learned Is Wrong—And What You Need To Know To Prosper in the New Economy." He goes back to the 1960s, citing a book, *The Human Side of Enterprise*. The author delineated Theory X and Theory Y of management.

Theory X was based on the notion that most people were not motivated and didn't want to work—you basically had to drive them to be productive. Theory Y said people were indeed willing to work, but you had to find ways to motivate them. If you take that one step further, you can look at the concepts of autocratic and democratic leadership. For a long time, people thought you had to be one or the other.

Through the 1930s and 1940s, autocratic leadership was definitely in style. You had a supreme being at the head of the department, or at the head of the company, who made most of the decisions. All the people came to that supreme being as subordinates, with ideas, problems or challenges. The supreme being made the decision and drove the direction.

In the 1950s and 1960s the idea of more democratic management became popular. In democratic management, the followers are involved in the decision-making process. People play on the decision-making field and develop a consensus. This has both a positive and a negative affect. On one hand, it develops ownership and energy in an idea that is developed by a group. On the other hand it can be very bureaucratic. When you create committees, it tends to add time and a lot of pabulum to the decision-making process.

So, if someone had an autocratic style of leadership, he told people what to do. That worked best with Theory X people—people who didn't want to be at work and basically needed to be told what to do. Theory Y people, on the other hand, want to work but need to be motivated. They would work best with someone who had a democratic leadership style.

However, as many people point out, there are times when an autocratic leader is definitely necessary. And there are times when a democratic leader is definitely necessary.

If you were sitting in a conference room and someone smelled smoke, you would not want him to say, "It seems there is some smoke in the room, let's form a committee to investigate the problem, come up with a consensus and vote on the decision." Here, you want an autocratic leader who says, "Follow me, we're going out the door."

In the case of a company picnic or holiday party, just because the boss likes hamburgers doesn't mean everyone should eat hamburgers. Perhaps using a democratic style and having a committee develop the ideas for the outing would be a good way to do it. Also, think of company mission statements: Who should create the mission for the company? Should it be the leader creating the mission in a vacuum? Or should there be some participation by the team?

Paul Hersey and Ken Blanchard created a concept called Situational Leadership. Basically, it doesn't matter whether you're an autocratic leader or a democratic leader, the proper course is based on the situation you're in. They broke people's tasks down into two areas: competence and commitment. Competence is the knowledge and skills to do the job. Commitment is the motivation and the confidence to do the job. Looking at both high and low amounts of these two areas creates four quadrants.

Competence = Knowledge and Skills
Commitment = Motivation and Confidence

The difference between knowledge and skill is the difference between being able to accurately describe an activity (knowledge), and the ability to perform the activity (skill). For example, many baseball fans can describe the process of turning a double play, or a medical student can describe the steps of a surgical procedure—they have the knowledge. But unless they have demonstrated their performance on the baseball field or in the operating room to the satisfaction of the leader, then they don't necessarily have the skill. Knowledge can be measured in a written or oral test. Skill must be measured by observing the person performing the skill.

In the areas of motivation and confidence, a person who is a novice swimmer may be motivated to swim over his head, but if he doesn't try it, he will never be able to demonstrate his confidence.

Motivation is easier to measure. You can simply ask someone if she is motivated to perform a task. An individual's motivation is related to how well the task or activity you are asking her to perform satisfies a need. We can never forget Maslow's hierarchy of needs. We are motivated to perform activities that satisfy our needs. That is why it is so important for us to identify others' needs and link those needs to the activities we want them to perform.

Measuring confidence is much more difficult. Few human beings will express a lack of confidence as readily as they will express a lack of motivation. Confidence is built by allowing people to perform a task in a low risk environment—like the child practicing his swimming stroke in shallow water.

To build confidence, you slowly and carefully raise the risk. You don't take the kid who can swim effectively in three feet of water and throw him into the deep end of the pool any more than you would ask a medical student to perform a complex surgical procedure. You move the kid to four feet, then five, and so on. You build confidence in people by allowing them to succeed in slowly increasing environments of risk.

The four quadrants (see Figure 1) would start with people who were very motivated to do the job: committed and confident, but lacking the basic knowledge and skills. This person is referred to as *The Enthusiastic Beginner.*

When people start to develop competence or skill, they encounter challenges that they never anticipated. Now some of their commitment either in the area of motivation or confidence begins to waver.

The second level is somewhat competent or *The Disillusioned Learner.* These individuals have varying levels of competence and commitment, but they haven't maximized both levels. Eventually, people develop the confidence to do the job if they're trained properly.

Situational Leadership Model

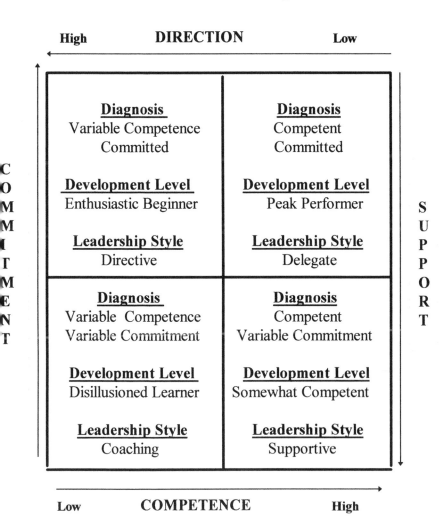

Figure 1

But with *Disillusioned Learners*, their motivation changes for the worse: it's not as much fun anymore, it's not as exciting, it's not as challenging. They're working twice as hard for half the satisfaction. Or they're really competent on what we might call the Triple A level in Minor League Baseball, but when they get to the Big Leagues, that confidence level goes down. So the competence is there, but the commitment wavers.

Finally, with intervention and help, people become *Peak Performers*. A *Peak Performer* is both competent and committed. When you lead a *Peak Performer*, you don't have to tell her what to do. She tells you what needs to be done. She tells you what to expect as an outcome. She's motivated and competent to do the job. She reports to you along the way while you stay out of her way.

Most people, when they think about being a leader, place themselves in the context of leading a group of enthusiastic beginners. "I'm going to take over an organization, and in my mind, most of those people really want to do the job, but they don't know anything about it. So I'm going to provide them with the things they need; I'm going to teach them how to do the job." But most teams are composed of people of various levels of competence and commitment.

The leadership requirement is to diagnose the level of development before the leader knows what kind of leadership style to provide for the subordinate. That's the leader's job.

Most people diagnose development level based on tenure. You must instead diagnose development level based on task—that is, the knowledge and skill levels for a particular task. Then you will be able to diagnose the commitment and the motivation.

THE 12-MINUTE MBA FOR DOCTORS

Situational leaders will diagnose the development level of their people in specific tasks and then provide a leadership style that the people need.

Let's take a look at a person who enjoys two particular activities: basketball and golf. In the area of basketball, she has the knowledge and skills of the game, she's motivated to play and competent in her game. So when she goes out to play basketball she can basically go out and play on her own. She can play with the kids or the neighbors, it doesn't matter. She may not be great but she is a *Peak Performer* in basketball at her own level.

When it comes to golf, however, which is something that is new for her, she's very motivated to play. She's very confident she can master this. She has the athletic ability to get around the golf course, but she doesn't have the knowledge or the skills yet. Her golf coach doesn't spend a lot of time pumping up her motivation or even her confidence level. Rather the coach spends a lot of time providing her with competence—helping her understand the game, the elements of her stroke and keeping her focused on the steps to hit the ball, not worrying where the ball goes. At this point, as an *Enthusiastic Beginner*, it doesn't matter how far she hits the ball. It matters whether her stroke is correct. If she tops the ball a little bit, or if she slices it or hooks it, that's not relevant at this point in her learning process. What's relevant is that she is getting her stroke down correctly.

If we really wanted to master a sport, like golf, there are more then a hundred steps in a proper golf swing. How does that golf pro interact with someone who has been playing a couple of years and has a 24 handicap? The time spent with the more advanced student would be much different because he is refining different skills.

He might be working on confidence in a particular shot so the coach might be working on motivating him to take 300 swings before he starts playing.

The leadership style is going to change because the development level of the follower is changing. A good leader is constantly diagnosing the development level of her people in the tasks they need to perform. The good leader does not assume they know how to do it; the good leader gives the followers the tools they need to perform.

A good leader will identify what the followers are missing and give it to them. If they need motivation, she gives them more motivation. If they need more skill, she gives them more skill. If they need more confidence, she reminds them of how good they were the last time they performed the task. She rebuilds their confidence.

A good leader becomes very focused on her people and what they are trying to achieve. The good leader then becomes less focused on her own goals and interests and desires, and more focused on the interests, goals and desires of the people she is meant to lead. She becomes a good situational leader who diagnoses development level and then provides the leadership style that is necessary for success.

Let's look again at leadership styles. Instead of autocratic and democratic, let's look at leadership styles as being directive and supportive. The directive mode is where I *tell* you what needs to be done. In the supportive mode I *ask* you what needs to be done.

Sometimes the leader needs to do a little "checkup from the neck up." He wants to see if his player's in the game. You see that in boxing all the time. You see it in the corner. One guy just took a pounding in the last round. He was ahead on all the scorecards. His coach is trying to find out why he's not focusing, or if he is able to focus. The trainer looks into the eyes of the boxer to see if he's in the game. A good trainer is a situational leader. When the boxer is doing poorly and his ego is damaged, the trainer pumps him up. Other times, when the boxer is doing really well, the trainer might say, "you're losing," because he wants the boxer to go out there and do better. Hopefully there is an intimate understanding between the trainer and the boxer— between the leader and the follower—as to what is needed in the incredibly emotional highs and lows throughout the course of a fight or a project.

In the course of perhaps 48 minutes—a 12-round fight with one minute between rounds—you are watching leadership happen. A boxing coach, like any leader, can help set goals and objectives. He can work on the boxer's deficiencies; he can work on the boxer's strengths. He can analyze and give feedback on the boxer's performance. But when it comes to throwing punches or delivering on a project, the boxer or player has to go out and do it himself.

The leader really doesn't play the game. Lots of times leaders have been peak performers, but when you look at the world of coaching, you tend to find the great coaches were not superior performers. They tended to be middle-of-the-road guys. They may not have been physically as capable, but they understood the game. They achieved beyond their physical capabilities and went on to become great coaches. They willed themselves to play at a high level. They were smart and aggressive and driven. Gifted people don't always know what it takes to teach the job because they learned naturally.

So what does it take to lead? Some of the greatest leaders had to work the hardest to perform in their chosen endeavor. The best leaders—the ones who achieve success for their organizations—are able to diagnose what their people need and give it to them. They may not be expert at all the tasks necessary for success, but they have the ability to diagnose what their people need from their leader and to give it to them.

Part of understanding management and leadership is understanding the movement of people along this development continuum toward peak performance. Wouldn't it be great if a team were composed of all peak performers? Management would be really easy. However, if a manager applies the wrong leadership style to a person at the wrong point in her development level, he will either frustrate the follower or become frustrated himself.

If I delegate a task to an *Enthusiastic Beginner* or someone with some competence who is not yet capable to do the job, I frustrate both of us. He is not going to get the job done; he is going to be frustrated with his performance and so am I. If I over-manage a person who has moved along the line to peak performance, then I really frustrate that person. It makes a team member upset if someone is telling her what to do when she already knows how to do the job.

Motivation, although sometimes an over-used term, is an incredibly important component of peoples' performance. If I am motivated to do something, my level of energy and performance often exceed the level of others who are not motivated or who are only slightly motivated. When I can motivate someone by linking the activity to his hierarchy of motivators, he may exceed my expectations of performance.

Motivation is a very interesting aspect of human behavior. People have a hierarchy of motivators that changes over time. Life situations tend to change one's hierarchy of motivators. Once you identify another's motivators, you can link those motivators to an activity you want him to perform. But be careful, over time and changes in situations, a person's motivation hierarchy can change.

Instilling confidence in others is an important aspect of being the leader. If you diagnose a lack of confidence in a subordinate to perform a task or activity, you need to remind that person how well she performed in the past in similar activities. If my child has learned to swim and is now competing with others, I may want to remind him how well he has performed in the past and to ignore the other people and concentrate on his stroke mechanics rather than worrying about his competitors. I want to build his confidence based on his own past success while I try to minimize his trepidation about the competition. Always remember that confidence is built on success, not failure. Failure can be a good teacher, but it is a lousy confidence builder.

Chapter 3

Teamwork

Throughout our entire lives we are involved in teams. As little kids, we're on teams in school. Better readers are together, middle readers are together and lower readers are together. We play sports from a young age where we are exposed to team behavior and team environments. Various dynamics evolve when you have young people trying to learn skills and participate in groups.

Even though we are oriented to team behavior through experiences as children, it's funny that when we get to the organizational area in work—particularly as it relates to the medical school environment and hospitals, which tend to be hierarchical—the development of teams is often contradictory to the daily function of individuals. Because the environments of medical school and residency are primarily competitive, it is difficult to expect people to work naturally in teams.

In seminars with hundreds of people, I have led team activities in which we quantified that team performance is always better than individual performance on achieving goals and objectives. In fact, 95 percent of the time we've demonstrated that team performance exceeds even startling individual performance.

We can look to many examples in life and work where no one person in the group is greater than the rest, but collectively their performance is exceptional. For example, look at the Yankees of the late 1990s. Some of the members were real stars, but the reason the Yankees functioned as a great team was that each of the parts functioned in a good team environment. Each player performed his role and tasks in a way that helped the team achieve as a whole.

Here's another example: The Eco-Challenge, a cross-country race held every year. Groups of people take on nature. They climb mountains, they ride bikes, they go down rapids and rivers, they hike through treacherous terrain and it takes six to twelve days to achieve these goals.

A few years ago Team Internet won the Eco-Challenge. These were people who had never met before. They were selected for their individual performances in each of the events. Each was an expert in one of the events.

That team was successful even beyond the other teams who had practiced together. The team had all of the five components of a good team, which we will get into shortly.

There are countless examples in business and sports

that demonstrate peak team behavior. In selling, if you look at a group of salespeople in a market selling to hospitals or to schools, the performance of each individual affects the others in the group. Someone who doesn't have a good team approach can bring down the whole team. This works in a medical office too. If the receptionist is negative toward the patient, then the patient's experience, regardless of the great medical treatment that was provided, will be a negative experience.

Although part of it is "every man for himself," let's take the hospital marketplace from a salesperson's perspective. There are key institutions in a given area that must be obtained as customers for the business to be successful. These are the leaders—the organizations that others look up to. Very often this key institution may be one salesperson's account, but everyone in that region will benefit if the group gets that business. Bringing everyone together to accomplish a mutual goal helps everyone win.

In the operating room, teamwork is imperative. In any given operation you have a primary surgeon, an assistant surgeon, a scrub nurse, a circulating nurse and residents who are involved in the case. Everyone has a very specific role. Everyone has to perform her role with an equal amount of intensity and commitment for the outcome to be successful.

Notice how the quality of work changes between the beginning and the end of a rotation for residents. At the beginning of rotations, teams will change. The performance of the group is less effective at the beginning than at the end of the rotation when people have had a chance to work with each other.

Team building is not often intuitive. We are brought up with a sense that "I am the most important thing on earth and I need to achieve for me." But through socialization, we learn to work together for everyone's benefit. The cave men, for example, learned when they hunted the woolly mammoth that no one man could bring down the woolly mammoth. It took a team to do it. The cooperation of people for survival and for success evolves into a team.

You can build a winning team. In any organization where people need to work together to achieve an objective—whether that's the profitability of the institution, the success of a surgical procedure on a patient, or the successful running of a bank, real estate company or law firm—the leader has to determine how to build a winning team.

There are five components of a successful team:

1. **Leadership**
2. **Defined Roles**
3. **Clear Objectives**
4. **Communication**
5. **Trust**

Let's look at these individually:

1. Every team needs a leader. That leader fulfills certain roles. Number one, the leader has to communicate the vision and the mission of the group. He also has to keep the team moving in the direction of the goal it hopes to achieve.

At times the leader has to remind people, either through positive reinforcement or negative reinforcement, that maybe they are getting off track, that they have to get back on track. They have to fulfill their roles for the team to achieve its mission or to win.

The leader is the person who creates the framework in which the team will move forward. It's a lot like the coach on the sidelines. The coach creates the game plan for the team, yet the coach doesn't play the game.

Very often the leader needs to be a coach; he needs to be someone who teaches the members of the team their roles. He needs to help them set goals and objectives and set up a strategic and tactical plan. At times the leader needs to step back and let each member of the team perform.

You see many small companies that succeed up to a point and then begin to fail. Usually the failure comes when that leader—who is, in essence, the business—controls and manages everything about that growing organization to the point where nothing moves forward. The company has reached a point where the leader needs to allow other people to make critical decisions. People are stagnated because they must look to the leader to make a decision even though they are capable of making the decision. The leader needs to know when to delegate the authority to make decisions to capable subordinates.

This leader needs to allow other people to be the leader in certain situations. If you go back to the Eco-Challenge, the strength of Team Internet was there was no one leader; everyone was a leader in his own area. In building a team, the leadership role can change, and that's perfectly fine, but someone must always fill the role of the leader.

2. Each member must have a defined role. Everyone needs to know what is expected of her in order to be successful. Very often the leader will help define roles, but in a really good team the members participate in defining roles. Not only do they then more fully understand their own roles, they also understand the roles of the other members of the team, which is very important.

The definition of roles can become a collective activity; it's not necessarily a one-on-one activity. In little league, when youngsters are learning about baseball and Joey is going to play first base, everyone learns what Joey is going to do at first base. Everyone learns Joey's role, as well as the roles of the second baseman and shortstop and on and on. That's a very important aspect of the definition of roles—you need to understand not only what's expected of you, but also what's expected of your teammates—if you expect to be successful.

3. Set clearly defined objectives. Probably the biggest mistake most leaders make, either with teams or within organizations, is failing to identify the objectives. When objectives are not clearly defined, they become abstract or even ethereal. People think they understand the goals, but each person's perception might be different.

There are two levels of goals. The strategic plan is the overall goal or objective of the team: to win the game, for example. That's certainly a strategic goal. Within strategies are tactics. Each big goal is broken down into a series of smaller goals. This way, people know they are tracking toward the ultimate objective, and that is the success of the team.

People should understand the objectives well enough that they can talk about them with each other. At times, in a team activity, one person will have to rise up and say to the rest of the team, "Hey, have we forgotten our objective here? We seem to be moving, but not in our original direction."

Now the team steps back, redefines its goals and understands clearly where it is going and when it has arrived. Harry Truman said the greatest job on earth was being a farmer plowing a field behind a mule. People were curious as to how that could be. He said the great thing about plowing a field is you know where you've been, you know where you're going and, most importantly, you know when you're done. Teams must understand all these pieces of the process.

4. Keep communication open. Successful team-work requires communication among the team members. You can see teams break down when the members don't communicate. We learn as kids playing basketball that when you are defending a player and he gets away, you have to communicate with your team that you have lost your defensive position on this person and someone needs to pick him up. You see it in baseball when an infielder and an outfielder are going after the same fly ball. There has to be communication between them as to who is going to catch the ball and what role the players are going to perform for that play.

The leader must create an environment in which people can communicate openly and express ideas, yet at the same time control the amount of communication to make sure it is pertinent to the team objective.

5. No team can ever succeed without trust. Members of the team must be able to trust their peers to fulfill their roles and be there for them. If you examine the world of mountain climbing, this can be a life or death component. For example, look at the people who died on the summit of Mount Everest several years ago. Mountain climbing is definitely a team activity. A rope ties every member of the climbing group to the others. If one person falls off the mountain, the job of the rest of the team is to hold tight to make sure that person doesn't fall to his death.

How can you trust someone with your life if you don't trust him as a team member? Most of the outward-bound programs have trust as an integral component. It would be silly to enter into a team activity and expect that trust will occur naturally. We all have our own goals and objectives. Very often one member of a team will want to excel beyond the level of his teammates. That's his individual objective. The leader has to create an environment of trust and talk about it. The leader has to identify the importance of trust and explain what it means to the success of the team. Trust means that if someone is not fulfilling his role, he can trust his teammates to tell him openly that he has let down the team in this particular task—and then not take it personally. This has to be accepted as good teamwork.

Also, the team has to have an outlet and a way to resolve issues of trust. First, the leader needs to ask, "How are we going to trust each other? Give me some feeling from the group about trust and some examples of where trust has worked for you in a team. Also, give me examples of where a lack of trust broke down a team."

Get the team members to talk about trust and define what it really means to them. Trust to one person means something different than trust to another person. Team members can only be on the same page if they have a common definition of trust. For trust to work, teams sometimes have to take a trust "time out." They have to review agreements and perhaps clarify them. Team members can evaluate how they have fulfilled their commitments to the team's goals and objectives. One team member might say she demonstrated trust by performing three certain tasks; another might say she let the team down by going on vacation during a crisis.

My experience has shown that in order to take the five components of teamwork seriously, the leader has to take "time out" to allow these processes to occur. They are not going to occur naturally.

Chapter 4

CONFLICT RESOLUTION

Conflict is a part of human nature and certainly a part of American history. When you are the leader of a team or an organization, resolving conflict quickly becomes a very important skill.

In fact, conflict has an economic impact on companies. The American Management Association has identified that middle managers in corporate America spend about 20 percent of their time resolving conflict. That's about one day a week.

Say your company has about 100 middle managers earning $80,000 per year, that's $8 million per year in budgeted cost. The cost, if 20 percent of their time is spent in conflict, is $1.6 million on that line item alone. I think we'd all agree you'd rather have an extra day a week to do productive things—or an extra $1.6 million-plus to spend more wisely.

As you move up in an organization, you can spend even more time resolving conflict. When I was Vice President of Sales at U.S. Surgical, I spent 80 percent of my time resolving conflict, both within the organization and outside the organization. It becomes very frustrating for a leader to spend most of his time in the middle of other people's arguments. Let's look at a typical day:

- Your two sons are fighting over a toy or if they're older, who's going to use the car.

- Your daughter and wife are arguing over what your daughter is going to wear to school.

You are probably at work already, but you get a page from your wife, exasperated over the kids, and your response is, "Just deal with it." OK, you may have avoided the argument, but now your spouse is angry with you and I guarantee you will pay later, and you know it.

Now, let's take a typical day at work:

- At the hospital, there's a disagreement between two residents.

- The O.R. director has just bumped one of your cases.

- A patient ate that morning.

- Your colleagues are deeply engaged in a battle for a new piece of equipment for the O.R.

- Your book chapter is due and the staff who were told to edit it just ignored your request.

- Your office calls with a complaint that two insurance claims have been denied and you have to call
the company to argue your case.

- Your lawyer calls about a pending malpractice
claim.

- Your secretary gets into it with your department
chairman's secretary and is threatening to quit.

After a long day of surgeries interspersed with
conflict engagements, you return home where the same
arguments from this morning await you only now your
spouse is also angry with you for your comment, "Just
deal with it."

OK, I bet you're thinking that this was nothing. You
deal with five or ten times that amount of conflict each
and every day. And you are probably right.

So you are probably thinking, "So what, conflict is a
part of every organization and every profession."
That's true, yet there are strategies and methods for
dealing with conflict that can have a very positive
effect. In fact, when people begin to understand how
they act in conflict situations, see alternative positions,
and work toward collaborating or creating win-wins,
that conflict, which is generally non-productive, can
become productive.

Kenneth Thomas and Ralph Kilmann, of UCLA and
the University of Pittsburgh, respectively, have studied
the area of conflict. They have created, in my experience, one of the best tools for understanding the nature
of conflict and the roles people play in a conflict
situation. In fact, their model has been used for years to

teach people in organizations about dealing with conflict. Their model allows individuals to identify their own conflict modes and those of others within the organization, and take a minute to think about the value and cost of a conflict before they charge in to engage.

Conflict is defined as any situation in which your concerns or desires differ from those of another. It can manifest itself as a difference of opinion or a heated argument. The difference depends on the importance of the issue and the amount of energy you put into achieving your goals.

There are five basic modes that humans take in a conflict. Each of these modes is really based on two very simple issues:

- **Assertiveness**: The degree to which one seeks to satisfy his own concerns.

- **Cooperativeness**: The degree to which one is willing to satisfy the needs of the other person.

If we put assertiveness and cooperativeness on an x/y axis (Figure 2), we can begin to define the five conflict modes. Now it is equally important to understand there are two forces that define the conflict mode you choose: skill and situation.

Skill refers to your perceived ability to succeed at the chosen conflict. If for example you find yourself in a conflict with someone who has superior debating skills or perhaps superior size strength and speed (obviously this would be a conflict taken to the extreme), you may choose a different mode than your tendency.

Also, the situation may dictate your mode. If you

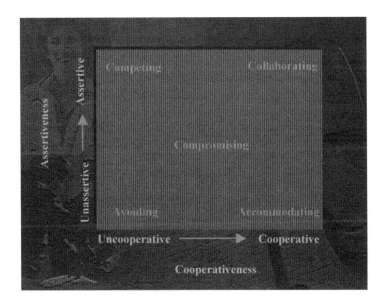

Figure 2

are in a debate with your boss, you probably will take a different mode than if you were in the same debate with a peer.

The key rule to remember is there is no one mode that is correct, it is situational. The truly successful conflict handler is the one who chooses the correct mode for her skills and in the correct situation.

Understanding yourself is important, but through understanding all the conflict modes, you are better

45

prepared to handle conflicts that are occurring in your family, your organization, or with your subordinates. In fact, the great thing about understanding the conflict modes is you have plenty of opportunities to observe others and identify which modes are used correctly or incorrectly.

Let's look at the five conflict modes. If we look at our x/y axis, we see the first mode as being high in assertiveness and low in cooperativeness. This mode we call Competing. It is really, "my way or the highway." People who are high competitors are quick to engage in any and all conflicts. This mode does have some very positive applications:

- In emergencies, where quick decisive action is often necessary.

- In issues where unpopular courses of action need implementation.

- In issues that are vital for organizational welfare and you know you are right.

- To protect yourself from people who try to take advantage of your good nature.

The problem with high Competitors is they are often surrounded by "yes" people, because people have learned it is dangerous to disagree with them. Subordinates may lack an opportunity to develop by asking the appropriate questions and offering possible suggestions that are divergent from the leader's.

Also, think about the people you want around you. Isn't it frustrating when you're engaged with a high

Competitor who wants to take every issue and everything you say to the mat?

The next mode we'll examine is the Avoider. This person is both low on assertiveness and low on cooperativeness. A wimp you might say. Yet Avoidance is a successful mode in a variety of situations:

• When an issue is trivial or there are more important issues to deal with.

• When you perceive no chance of satisfying your concerns.

• When the potential damage of conflict outweighs the benefits of resolution.

• To let people cool down.

• When you need to gather more information.

• When others can be brought in to resolve the conflict more effectively.

Overuse of Avoidance might make you appear to be weak or lacking an opinion. If you under-use this mode, you find yourself involved in even the most trivial issues. Knowing when to avoid a conflict gives you tremendous power and allows you to deal with the truly important issues.

Next, we'll deal with the mode of Accommodating. Here we see a high amount of cooperativeness and a low amount of assertiveness.

The Accommodator is a good role for the following situations:

- When you realize you are wrong.

- When the issue is more important to the other person.

- To build social credits for other issues, that is, politicking.

- To preserve harmony.

- To allow subordinates to experiment and learn.

Overuse of Accommodating may result in others seeing you as a kiss-ass. It can deprive you of influence. When you don't use accommodating behaviors you may have trouble building goodwill with others. Others may regard you as self-serving and unreasonable. People may think you don't know when to give up.

Now let's talk about the remaining two conflict styles. First there is the style of Compromising. Compromising does have some advantages:

- When goals are moderately important but not worth the effort to fight.

- When two powers of equal importance are strongly committed to exclusive goals.

- To achieve temporary settlements to complex issues.

- To arrive at expedient solutions under time pressure.

- As a back-up mode when collaboration or competition fails.

The overuse of Compromising may cause you to overlook the larger issues. The process of bargaining and trading creates a political environment as in government where every position is balanced by giving up some power. Conversely, the lack of use of well-planned and placed compromise may leave large and important issues unsettled.

The final conflict mode is Collaborating. This mode is equally strong in assertiveness and cooperativeness. It is the ultimate win-win negotiation. It is an important position in the following situations:

- Finding an integrative solution when both sets of concerns are too important to be compromised.

- When your objective is to learn.

- To merge insights from people with different perspectives on a problem.

- To gain commitment by incorporating others' concerns into a consensual decision.

- To work through hard feelings of disparate parties.

The overuse of collaborating behavior may actually limit the number of issues that can be resolved. Collaboration takes a lot of work and a commitment on both sides of the issue to work toward win-wins.

The lack of initiative in creating collaborative conclusions may cause the best solution to be missed. Win-wins are important when dealing with big important issues where there are conflicting positions.

Now I hope you see that there is no one style or position to take in a conflict situation. It is important to take a moment and evaluate the importance of the issue. Next, take a moment and evaluate the style that the other person has taken in the issue. Once you understand your competitor's style, you can evaluate the smartest and most practical position to take in regards to the issue.

As a leader, it is important to understand the role that conflict takes in your organization. Are the conflict situations beneficial to finding the right solutions to problems, or are they obstacles to the fulfilling of your organization's goals and objectives?

The leader of an organization should work to reduce unproductive conflict in the organization, yet it is important for divergent opinions and positions to be expressed and explored. It must be the leader's goal to evaluate the amount of conflict and make sure it is not crippling organizational progress.

At times, a leader must choose to take a conflict style that adds to productivity. Alfred Sloan, who brought General Motors to supremacy over Ford, used conflict to challenge and alter prevailing wisdom and prevent the creation of stagnant thinking in his organization. Therefore, the lesson of this session is that conflict is both a good and a bad thing. It is the leader's responsibility to turn conflict into a positive.

As you reflect on how conflict resolution leads to greater productivity, take the ideas and concepts I've discussed, do something to put them into action. The Thomas-Kilmann instrument is available from booksellers, and there are many organizational consultants who can come to your organization and conduct half-day sessions on conflict.

Through these sessions all the members of your team will learn about themselves and their peers and team members. Remember, the engagement and resolution of conflict is not intuitive. Just because you are an intelligent person doesn't mean you have the skill to understand and resolve conflict. This is another skill that is, as Steven Covey says, is "common sense but not common practice." Great leaders identify what they don't know and bring it into their organizations. It is your responsibility as a leader to diagnose what your organization needs and provide it.

Now you probably are waiting for me to tell you how to deal with conflict at home. I can tell you I have found only two things that work. Avoid all conflicts at home and, if that fails, use the sixth and less known style of conflict resolution: Beg for Mercy.

You have to ask yourself how much time you spend resolving conflict, either at work or at home. Parents can spend a lot of time resolving conflicts between children, between children and the other parent and, of course, with their spouses. No one enjoys that, but we do it all the time.

Conflict will occur during the performance of a team. You do not want that conflict to cripple the team. Some conflict can be good, because we learn from discomfort. We learn to hunt because we are hungry. We learn to write because we have to store ideas. We learn to speak because we have to communicate.

A little conflict in a team, placed strategically and resolved, is very fortifying to the team. It shows team members they can confront challenges and overcome them. It's a real confidence builder.

How a leader deals with conflict is very important. You can't ever have a team that does not face conflict. You don't want a team that is always in conflict, but you want to engage in a little bit of conflict at strategic points to allow the team to grow and develop.

Conflict resolution is important in both business and families. It sets the table for greater productivity all around. It's something that can be learned.

Chapter 5

STRATEGIC AND TACTICAL PLANNING SKILLS

Every organization, whether it's a for-profit company or a non-profit organization, starts out with a mission. Usually that mission spells out what that company wants to be over the next five years. "What are we here to do?" The mission might be to improve the health of the general population or to add value for stockholders.

Mission statements are usually short statements of hope. In the best companies, everyone on staff believes in the company's mission statement.

There's a company, for example, that started in the pacemaker business. It's a multibillion-dollar medical device company, Metronic and is a mission-driven concern. When you walk into the corporate office, there is a large glass wall with the mission written on it. That mission is translated into every language in which the company does business around the world.

Every single person in that company, from the CEO to the people who clean the offices, not only knows the mission but also believes in it.

A mission has everything to do with the values of the organization. "We're here to do something good, and that mission is a part of our values structure." A mission can also address how we treat our customers and how we treat our fellow employees. It shows what we believe in.

No matter what kind of mission statement you have, it is imperative that you also have a strategic plan. Your plan must be aligned with your mission. And now, instead of being vague like the mission, the plan puts some very concrete steps into action over the next three to five years.

Strategic plans are the road maps to help a company achieve its long-term goals. Usually, strategic plans are created by the officers of the company, the top decision makers. They come together in some venue and create a list of plans to achieve the mission. It might, for example, be a marketplace strategy.

In order to improve worldwide health, which might be the mission of a surgical device company, the strategic plan would be to manufacture top quality products, to identify the needs of the customers in the marketplace, or to build cost-effective products that help surgeons or physicians to provide better health care for their patients. The strategic plan starts to take the vague mission of improving health and put some concrete words around it.

For a strategic plan to be successful, it has to be communicated—just like a mission statement. Take Medtronic as an example: everyone in that organization understands the mission. In turn, everyone should also understand the long-term strategic plan. "How are we going to go about achieving the mission? What are we going to do in the marketplace? Who are we going to target as potential customers? How are we going to develop and deliver our products?" How do the leaders empower the staff and get them involved in the mission and the strategic plan?

All employees should participate in some way in the development of the mission statement. Should everyone be able to write a mission statement that is voted on and adopted? Probably not. However, getting more team members to participate—not only in understanding but also in creating the mission statement—is an important component in the development of a business. Every single person who has a part in this process develops ownership in the company's goals and has a stake in achieving the mission.

Take a small service business, perhaps a legal or medical practice. Wouldn't it be terrific if, in forming the business, every one of the 20 or so employees had some part in defining the mission? If they did, would they not feel better about the tasks they had to perform at work, even the difficult or challenging duties?

The best strategic plans incorporate all the key people from the get-go—as the plans are developed. If you have a five-year strategic plan in which many people have been involved, would they not feel ownership in that plan and want to be around for five years?

The problem with most bigger companies is that the missions and plans are created in a vacuum. They are put together by the officers or the top two or three people. The mission and the strategic plan might end up on a plaque that no one takes seriously. It might be printed and distributed or even carved into wood, yet no one in the organization lives to the mission or even talks about it. It's a one-time event created for the people, instead of a living document created by the people.

If you talk about effective teamwork in small, service-oriented companies, then you are talking about every person in that organization doing much more than her defined role. How can a person live this mission if she has just been given some document from above? How can employees live this mission and enact those plans if they're not part of strategic planning?

How many times have you called a doctor's or lawyer's office and you know in your heart and soul that if you got that doctor or lawyer on the phone he'd want to talk with you. But it seems the only goal of the person at the other end of the phone is to get rid of you?

I noticed that when we moved to northwest Connecticut in trying to find new physicians. The first question they asked was, "Who's your insurance carrier?" They didn't say, "Welcome to the area; we're happy that you're here. What are you looking for in a doctor?" Their only concern was whether we had the means to pay. When we told them the name of our insurance carrier, at least a third said, "Well, we don't do business with that insurance company, thank you very much. Good-bye."

In fact, few of them said, "Thank you very much."

How can you build a medical practice that way? We hope your mission is to improve the health of the people in your town. We hope part of your strategic plan is to attract new patients so you can keep the business going. And yet the person who answers the phone is turning people away.

There's often a disconnect—whether it's a big company or a small business—between the principals' goals and objectives and what people do daily on the front lines. The way to eliminate that difference is to have everyone participate in either the creation of a strategic plan, or, more importantly, sit down twice a year with everyone in the company and see how you're doing with this plan you created together.

Maybe you came to work for the group two years after the plan was created. That doesn't mean you should be disconnected from the strategic plan. As the principal of the company, I need to connect you to the plan. It would be foolish to rewrite the plan for every new employee. But we can meet twice a year and see how we are doing. Are we achieving our goals and objectives? Are we delivering our service in such a way that our customers come back for more? Are we attracting more customers or patients to our practice because of the way we live up to our strategic plan? Is everyone in agreement with our plan? Can we identify objections or differences?

The good leader doesn't just create a plan. The good leader incorporates the staff in a framework to live up to that plan. A good leader needs to bring the people in the organization together periodically and ask how the team is doing in achieving the strategic plan. The leader needs to ask the group for ideas for improvement or change if the strategic plan isn't succeeding. By doing this, each team member will see his participation in the plan and, hopefully, have ownership in the accomplishment of the plan and goals.

There's a difference between a strategic plan and a tactical plan. A strategic plan is a long-term plan: what we're going to achieve and how we're going to achieve it. A tactical plan is a formulation of short-term contingencies in response to a changing environment. That tactical plan might vary from the path of the strategic plan, but it has to at least go in the same general direction.

Let's go back to that doctor's office. Suppose your goal was to have 1,000 patients on board in five years. Let's say you made that plan when all the insurance carriers were equally easy to do business with; you didn't have a problem with any particular carrier. But after you created that plan, one of the insurance carriers became more difficult to deal with. You decide you would rather not look for patients using that particular plan, but you might want to try to find more patients in the plans you are more comfortable dealing with.

Does that tactical change in your plan mean that anyone who calls up and is part of that particularly difficult insurance company is rejected out of hand? That would be ludicrous. Yet that's what people do.

Maybe you want to continue to attract patients from that plan, but you want to make them less important in your total mix. Maybe instead of that plan representing 30 percent of your business, you want it to represent 20 percent or 10 percent. Now you can pick and choose among those patients—not just shut them off at the door.

Those challenges come because very often the day-to-day operation of your business is not handled by a decision-maker. It's handled by someone who has been delegated to make a decision and who interprets that decision in her own way.

At the top we say we'd like to cut back on our use of X insurance company, but by the time it gets to the person answering the telephone it's translated into, "We're not going to do business with people who are covered by X insurance company." There's a big difference in the interpretation of our strategic plan between the executive level and the operational level.

Revenues and profits often suffer as a result.

How does an executive know what's really going on at the operational level? It's a very interesting challenge. At one company, my CEO, who was a very hands-on guy, would, from time to time, call customer service to see how customers were treated. He would take the time to make a phone call as if he were a customer. Who knows, maybe he had surrogates do this as well.

If you run a business, you need to check on customer service because you forget a basic point: It's not you who has the most contact with your potential customers—it's all those people who are operating your business. Those people then become one of the most important components of your business. They interpret your strategic plan for your potential marketplace. This component is even more critical with small, service-oriented businesses, particularly those which serve a community.

Big companies have systems of checks and balances. You've probably called a company before and heard a message that your conversation might be recorded. Everyone knows—both the customer and the employee—that someone is going to listen to what you say. Most big companies have systems that allow them to plug into ongoing conversations to ensure that each conversation is being handled in line with the strategic plan.

The bigger the company, it seems, the more sensitive the executives are to the image customers get when they phone in. In a smaller company that might have the principal just down the hallway, the owners might be even more concerned with business that walks in off the street. But very often, they're not.

If you walk into a car dealership, for example, what

do you notice? There are a bunch of salespeople with desks and there are some people with big glass windows who can see the sales floor. Often one of those offices is occupied by the owner of the company. Why do you think he wants to look out? He wants to make sure customers are being handled properly on the sales floor—that customers are being treated with respect and no one is turned away at the door.

Yet, in most professional practices, is the doctor or lawyer anywhere near that door? Is there any kind of window where she can see what is going on in her operation? Mostly not. The professionals are secured way back, hidden carefully in the bowels of the office, far removed from the customers who may be trying to get to them.

Some owners and executives create the gatekeepers and blockades because they don't want to be bothered with they day-in, day-out operation of the business. They don't want to be bothered with clients or customers. But we know, as consumers, that when you're doing business with someone in your community, you would like to see the president of the bank, the managing partner of the law firm, or the head of the medical practice from time to time.

Think of your favorite local restaurant. Isn't it a nice feeling when the owner comes to sit at your table, pays special attention to you and, in a subtle way, thanks you for spending your money with him? Don't you even look forward to going back the next time?

Why is it more fun to do business with a small local bank or law firm or medical practice than with a big conglomerate? You feel important, you feel like your business means something to that bank. If the president walks on the floor and talks to the tellers, you can see the attitude of the leadership of the company. You can sense the attitude of the leadership of a company by the way you are treated when you walk in the door.

If the principal of the company makes himself more available to the customer, then the people who work for him tend to think the customer has more value. They see that the customer or patient is not just someone coming in there trying to give them more work. That is important to any small business owner—doctor, lawyer, banker or auto retail store. Every person who walks in might be there to do something for them. It seems business owners and staff are more afraid of what people are trying to do to them, rather than welcoming what people might do for them. That's why they try to avoid some contact.

In terms of good strategic planning, it's critically important for the leader of the organization to communicate the strategic plan not only to the employees, but also to the customers—just like the good restaurateur.

Wouldn't it make sense that when a customer walks into a business, he sees a mission statement on the wall? What do you feel when you see that? Maybe that they're proud of what they're doing; maybe they know what they're doing.

Do you ever compare the service you get to what the mission statement says? You do that by nature. Who is this company? What are they about? Why do I want to do business with company X, Doctor Y or Lawyer Z? Because they publicly stand up and say, "This is what we're all about." When you walk into that office, people treat you with the same respect they articulate in their mission statement. That's part of their strategic plan.

All companies have an image. Johnson & Johnson, a $20-billion-plus business, is thought of as the baby company. Much of the company's business is in pharmaceuticals and medical and surgical supplies. Only one part of their business is consumer products, and a very small part of it is the baby-supply business.

J&J has a tremendous image. People pretty much believe that when Johnson & Johnson does something, they do it right, because who would hurt a baby?

When J&J had a problem with tainted Tylenol, what did they do? They took every single bottle of Tylenol off the shelf. They replaced every single one with a product in new packaging with an improved safety level.

J&J didn't cause the problem. Some nutcase put cyanide in a few of their pills. Yet the company's image is that the consumer counts and that they care about you. They fulfilled that mission and image by how they handled the crisis—demonstrating that they were protecting the consumer.

How did people feel about Johnson & Johnson after the crisis? They felt better about the company. Tylenol outsells every other product of its kind, and it's really a simple product with many competitors. People believe in the name of the company and what's behind it. Every great company has an image that the consumer understands and policies that the consumer believes in.

When you're a service business, you need to develop loyalty. You need a mission. You need your people to live up to your strategic plan. Your customer needs to know that plan, and your staff needs to handle the customer with the same level of professionalism that you would deliver.

That customer will turn around and walk away, and you'll never know why, if you fail in these key areas.

Remember:

- **The mission is what we want to be.**
- **The strategic plan is how we are going to get there.**
- **The tactical plan is what we are going to do when confronted by short-term challenges.**

As the leader, you need to make sure your people are delivering on these strategic and tactical plans. And wouldn't it be even better if your customers not only knew what your plan was, but also gave you feedback on whether you were delivering the service or product?

Just the act of asking, "How are we doing? Have we delivered on our commitments? Have we satisfied your needs?" makes the customer feel better. When was the last time a doctor or a lawyer or even a banker asked you questions like this?

Forget about it.

That's the problem with most small service businesses in the professional sector. They don't have a mechanism to find out whether their consumers are satisfied. They don't have a mechanism to identify whether their people are living up to their policies and procedures—or, more importantly, to their strategic plan. A lot of them don't even think about it.

When an unsatisfied customer walks out the door, your business ends. It might not end today, because you have enough sustained business to carry you forward. But the death of your business begins the day those customers stop coming back.

The time to find out how you are doing is when customers are taking advantage of your service.

Chapter 6

NEGOTIATING SKILLS

Historically, negotiating has been viewed as a battle between warring parties. That's the wrong way to look at it; it's unproductive.

As a kid, I remember seeing reports on TV about the negotiations between the United Auto Workers and General Motors. They would shut down the auto plant right on TV. The image I always had of those negotiations was of stiff men in business suits—opponents sitting across from each other at a big desk.

I remember the images of the Vietnam peace negotiations. Again, it was a big table. On one side was the enemy; on the other side was the alleged good guys. They all wore business suits and they all sat stone-faced, looking angry.

Growing up, my concept of negotiation was confrontation—adversarial. One side had one opinion, the other side had a different opinion, and no one wanted to give up anything.

They sat there for days and days and days at the peace negotiations and no one said anything. The first person who spoke lost; if you gave a concession, that meant you lost.

As a grownup living in the business world you are negotiating all the time. Whether it's for a lease, a salary or a promotion, or with a customer or a vendor—if you handled these negotiations like the old peace talks or labor talks, where two sides sat at a table with folded arms and didn't say anything, you'd never get anywhere.

Here's a different way to look at it: The goal of a successful negotiation is mutual satisfaction. The old paradigm of the two opposing sides who don't want to give anything up just doesn't work. Both sides can win if the goal is mutual satisfaction.

When I first began to negotiate with academic medical centers, I encountered a very well-educated surgeon who had a high position at a university. He had written hundreds of scholarly articles and obtained many millions of dollars in grants.

The surgeon said he had a great plan, he would like me to be a partner, but if I could not, he would go to the competition. I was amazed. This person had no clue about win-win negotiations. His first act in discussing a deal was to threaten his potential partner.

This helped me realize an important fact:

Negotiating is not an intuitive skill. It must be learned.

Most of us do not have a forum in which to learn win-win negotiations. We learn from watching TV or listening to our parents or listening to stories about negotiations where it's about "me winning and you losing."

There is a time in a negotiation to pull out a hammer, but that time certainly is not in the opening volley. It's not a great way to begin a process that could be a win-win for both parties.

You might want to pull out that hammer if there's a stall in the negotiations. Or you might want to pull out that hammer if you are seriously considering going to the competition and the other side is showing little interest in working with you.

The person who pulls out this hammer prematurely, loses. He's played his strongest hand up front. You know what his cards are.

On the other hand, if you're his opponent, you might know something about the competition and their willingness—or unwillingness—to participate with him. You've done this negotiation many times before. You know how your competition acts. Your potential partner probably does not.

In a negotiation, you do not want to get emotional or angry. People who are angry get caught up in the emotion of the victory rather than the common sense of the win-win solution. You want to make the best and most logical business decision in the context of your partnership with the other side, whether that be a landlord, an employer, a vendor or a contracted service person.

I've seen companies give away much more than they have to because their negotiators are caught up in the battle to win. The deal should be more important than that fleeting feeling of victory.

Two elements are important in every negotiation. The first is the substance. What are we negotiating for?

The second element is the act or method of negotiating. You need to separate these components in order to effectively negotiate a win-win.

Consider these four principles:

1. **Whatever the outcome, our lives go on.**
2. **Focus on interests, not positions.**
3. **Generate a variety of solutions.**
4. **What are the results of our deal?**

Let's look at these points individually:

1. Whatever the outcome, our lives go on. We might meet another day. This is important in the world of business. You will likely meet this person again. You want to be able to maintain a relationship. The people are not the problem; the matter being negotiated is the problem. This brings to mind the old-style labor negotiations. Each side would talk to the press and say the most horrible things about the other side. They would berate the other side, call them crooks, liars, cheats and thieves. Then, when they reached an agreement, they would shake hands and pat each other on the back as though they were the best of friends. It always amazed me. I don't think that works well in business negotiations. It's better to separate the people from the problems.

Here's how I might soften a position, deflate anger and refocus on what I can deliver if the other person threatens to go to the competition:

"You have a right to go to the competition. If you want to go to the competition, I think you would be better off doing that. I would welcome a comparison with the competition. After you talk with them, let's get together and talk again to see if we can make this deal come together."

This happened a lot in my negotiations with medical centers. The money available from my company and from the competitor was similar, but the two corporate cultures were quite different. If the mission of the medical center was to be innovative, if they were looking to use better devices that we might develop, and if they were looking to move science forward in a very aggressive manner, then our corporate culture met those needs.

I could agree with this potential client that he would get the same amount of money, maybe even more, from our competitor. Agreeing is a very powerful tool in negotiation. I might say:

"Take a very close look at their financial offer. That would be my advice. But also take a very close look at their culture, at what kind of a partner they would be. How would they work with you and help you accomplish your mission?"

In some of the martial arts you use your enemy's attack and strength and transform it into your victory. This is a similar process in the interplay of power.

2. Focus on interests, not positions. In a given negotiation my position could be, "I want this deal for X price." I could become very passionate about protecting that position, arguing for that position and fighting hard for it throughout the negotiation. But is that really my interest? Is X right, or is X plus one still OK? If I can create a win-win, if X plus one creates a win for both of us even though I gave something up, isn't that a better deal than sticking to X?

Most of my negotiations in my professional life were with my boss. I negotiated for benefits, working conditions, assignments, salary, time off, perks.

Many people come to the table quite focused on a certain position. For example, a friend of mine negotiated for the position of chairman of surgery at a very prestigious medical center. At first, he was not the prime candidate. The medical center had gone outside and recruited someone with a big reputation. They were willing to pay a very large salary for this person. As it turned out, it seemed that person never intended to take the position, but was using the offer as leverage to cut a better deal back home.

After the medical center exhausted that recruiting effort, they came back to my friend. By that time, he had decided he didn't want the job, but their solicitation made him reconsider.

My friend was stuck, however, on the offer the medical center made to the outsider. The offer to my friend was significantly less.

He was focused on this number as a deal breaker. We discussed his strategy and looked at other soft-dollar incentives that might affect his daily duties and his life. These items had nothing to do with the big compensation number.

For example, could he ask them to pay for housing? That was part of the deal for the outsider. A $500,000 house with no mortgage is an after-tax benefit that before taxes would cost 40 percent more.

He could certainly keep fighting for the big number, but is that what he really wanted? With most employment negotiations, people get stuck on the number. Yet for many, income is not the prime motivator for taking the job in the first place. Other factors often are more important: the nature of the work, the people, the environment along with the opportunity for growth and advancement.

Yet from the time you walk in the door, negotiation can focus exclusively on what you're going to get paid. That should be farther down on the list. How many times a day do people in the professions think about how much they are getting paid? Once a need is satisfied, it no longer motivates people. Money is not necessarily high on the list of daily thoughts for high achievers—or, for that matter, on the list for many employees. Studies have shown that although people certainly care about their compensation, there are other vital issues that concern them as well.

Highly motivated professionals are concerned with other job-related issues. They want to enjoy their work and make a difference. They want to be challenged. They want to get better at what they do. They want to work with teams of other successful people.

At a certain level, the negotiation for income is fueled by your actual financial needs. Yet there's another level at which some define their self-worth. Some people argue you can never make enough. The cave men who hunted more lived longer and had more children. I guess they call that natural selection. But when you wake up in the morning, do you think about how much money you make? Or do you think about that once a week, or once a month when you pay bills?

Your prime motivators are what you think about every day. Will the new job satisfy those issues?

That's why I talk about focusing on interests and not positions. If you lock on to the position, "I need to make X and he wants to pay Y," then you and the potential employer both lose.

Why do you really want the job? Why do they really want you? Is it an economic reason, or are there other reasons? Look for ways around those financial issues and you will often end up with a very satisfying deal.

3. Generate a variety of solutions. Let's say in a negotiation we're stuck on the salary issue. We could stay locked on that issue and be like the Vietnam War negotiators sitting around with our arms folded and waiting for the other side to budge.

Another way is to set that salary issue aside for a bit. Then look at a variety of solutions that can create a win for both of us, such as the university hospital-owned housing. Instead of just salary, look at the total cost of living. If I can eliminate some of your cost of living by offering you a house rent free, you can eliminate some salary needs.

Other solutions could include the university helping you to attract and hire top-level employees. Perhaps you could hire a top-flight business administrator to help you run the business side, freeing you up for more creative endeavors—science and health care. Wouldn't it be better if you had a staff to take care of the concerns that might otherwise bog you down?

You will never explore these issues if you are stuck on a position. In good, win-win negotiations, we begin to look for solutions that may be "outside the box" of traditional issues.

4. What are the results of our deal? What criteria can we use to measure this deal? How can we look back and say we both won? Look into the future. If we cut this employment deal today, can we set up a situation where we come back in a year and measure the success of the deal? Let's set up a series of measurements of your effectiveness over the next 12 months. If you achieve those things, then you deserve the big number.

To develop good negotiation skills, you need to let go of your emotional need to win and think about how you can set up wins for both parties. Too often good deals for both parties break down because each party becomes too focused on winning. They want to be able to tell their friends and family how they won their deal, even though the victory, more emotional than practical, may give them very little of what they really want.

Let's face it, sometimes it is better to think about what you really want, long-term, than what will satisfy you today. If you really want that car that you are negotiating so hard to buy for $35,000 and the dealer wants $35,500, does that $500 difference really matter over the next five years? That difference breaks down to $100 a year—just under $9.00 a month. You probably throw $9.00 in change into your kid's piggy bank every month. Yet in the passion of trying to win a negotiation, you focus on the number rather than what you really want.

In negotiating with a professional negotiator, like the representative of an insurance company, you are up against an adversary who is an expert in negotiating. You are an expert in your field of doing surgery or providing patient care. Do you think you can win against a competitor who negotiates every day of his life? Probably not. You are better off trying to create a win-win rather than an all out win.

There are many tactical strategies in negotiating. The most important tool available to you in any negotiation is information. And, as in persuasive communication, you gain that information by asking questions. Information will help you achieve a win-win negotiation. So you have to use your probing skills. Ask lots of open-ended questions that lead to long answers. Once you get that information, identify ways for both of you to win.

Think about the negotiations you engage in at home. If you want to watch the final round of the Masters golf tournament on Sunday afternoon, isn't it better if you have spent the morning engaged in a family activity that satisfies everyone's needs? To get your time, you have to give time to others to fulfill their needs.

We negotiate almost every day. We negotiate time from other people; we negotiate effort from other people; and we give up our time and efforts to satisfy others so we can get what we want.

The reality of negotiating with a loved one is that we always compromise or collaborate to gain our needs. In a business situation it is the same. It is not about winning at the expense of our adversaries, it is about finding ways for both of us to win. This is the spirit behind the best negotiation. If we can find a way for both of us to win, then it is a successful negotiation.

There are many different strategies and tactics for negotiation. Most of these are known and practiced by the professional negotiators. There are several good books that focus on these tactics, some of which are listed in the Epilogue.

The most important thing to remember about negotiating is that information is power. The more you know about the needs and desires of your negotiating adversary, the better chance you have of creating a win-win. You also need to think like your adversary in order to understand her position. She may need the deal less than you do, equally, or more than you do. If you are looking to rent office space, and you notice that only 60 percent of the building is occupied, your chance of getting a better deal is far greater than if the building is 90 percent occupied.

If you are negotiating for a job in your area and the other candidates have to be moved in from out of town, you are in a much stronger position to negotiate because there is no cost to relocate you. You may be able to negotiate those dollars into your contract or show how you are a better choice because hiring you will ultimately cost the organization less.

Whatever the deal, you will need to live with it for a long time. Don't let the frustrations and emotions of a difficult negotiation live through the life of the contract. Regardless of the deal you finally cut, let the negotiation go and move on.

The purpose of the written contract is to have a document that defines the deal. This is important because the people on the other side may change, and any verbal agreements that haven't been documented may no longer apply.

One final important item in negotiation. Always have an outside authority, either real or imagined, that has to approve the deal. Never close the deal at the end of an emotionally trying session. Ask for the opportunity to check with your boss or your spouse or your administration, even if you are the final decision maker. It is too easy to get to the end of a deal and want to close it so badly that you make a concession that you will regret later. By being able to walk away from the table, for an hour or a day, and be sure you are satisfied, you may ensure years of satisfaction.

Chapter 7

UNDERSTANDING FINANCIAL ISSUES

By STEVEN STEARNS With CHARLES JOHNSON And ANDY THIBAULT

EDITOR'S NOTE: Steven Stearns is a portfolio manager and financial consultant with Salomon Smith Barney in Westport, Connecticut. Stearns is an engineering graduate of Princeton with an MBA from the Harvard Graduate School of Business Administration and a former Army officer. He has extensive corporate experience in the financial services, medical device, entertainment and real estate industries.

Charlie and I share the same frustration in how some subjects are taught. My frustration started when I was an engineering student in college. I also experienced frustration taking accounting and finance courses. We have a way of teaching technical matter from the bottom up. We really start at the component level and wear students out or bore them to death. Unfortunately, they don't get to see how an entire system works or how elements come together.

That became clear to me when I became a student at the Harvard Business School, which relies on a case-study method. I had to take a first-year accounting course along with CPAs who had been with the Big Six accounting firms for four to six years. They had to sit through this. They all had the same comment: "I learned more in this accounting course than I learned in four years of undergraduate accounting and four years of practice." That's because there is a better way of getting this information across: from the top down rather than from the bottom up.

The reality is, small businesses have the same problems as big businesses. The principles that make big business run well can also apply to small business, whether it is starting a new business, adding a new product, adding a new service or expanding into new markets. There is a process I have seen work very successfully in the big businesses I have been involved in and that I now apply to my own small business as a financial consultant and money manager.

The first step in the process is to really know your market. Ask yourself very specifically: What is it that I am trying to do and who am I trying to do it for?

The biggest error is in not being specific enough in defining the market in which you are going to participate. Even financial people make the mistake of not understanding some of these broader concepts.

The second step is to know who the decision makers are in your marketplace. I break those down into two groups: those who make the buying decisions and those who make the "no-more-buying" decisions. To put it on another level, the person dropping off and picking up the dry cleaning usually makes the decision to go to a specific cleaner. The person who starts yelling and screaming that the buttons are broken on all the shirts makes the "no-more-buying" decision.

When I worked at U.S. Surgical, they initially marketed directly to the surgeon. The surgeon made the buying decision. That was the person who tried the instrument and then told the procurement agent what and how many to buy. But in the course of three years, surgeons lost their absolute say-so in the purchasing process. In most organizations, a conglomerate purchasing agency took over, whether it was an HMO or a buying organization for a group of hospitals. The surgeons had less influence.

Sometimes the decision makers change very quickly. You have to decide whether you want to go to that business again to win the new decision makers, and then how you can compete effectively.

The third step is to know the criteria these people use to make decisions, and the weight they put on each requirement. It sounds simple, but people mess it up all the time, even extremely well-run companies.

It happened when I was working for Disney in California between 1990 and 1992 for the group that was planning new theme parks. Now before I start throwing stones at Disney, I have to say it is one of the best run companies I have ever encountered. But, in the process of planning a new theme park for southern California, they decided to build a theme park in Europe. This is where you learn not to let the financial numbers alone drive the decisions you make.

Disney had two possible sites for this park: one in France and one in Spain. There was a lot of negotiation with top government officials and a head-to-head competition between the two countries. Ultimately, Disney decided to put the park in France based on short term financial factors. The French government offered a financial package that was significantly better than Spain's. So off they went to build a $3 billion theme park in France.

The architect/MBA who was running our group said that before we did any more work, we should go to the archives and pull out the original studies that Walt Disney commissioned for the Orlando, Florida location. We found that 85 percent of the report on Orlando was weather data. The report focused on a location that was attractive and comfortable year-round. Walt Disney wanted a warm, sunny climate.

As we looked at this data, the Disney Co. was pouring billions of dollars into Paris. I don't know if you've been to Paris in November, December, January, February or March—it's cold, rainy and nasty. So we looked at each other around the table and said "Paris is going to be a disaster." For the most part, it has been a disaster. It hasn't been an impediment to Disney, because Disney doesn't own most of the park; it's owned by a separate holding company.

Big companies make big mistakes. Why? In this case, Disney forgot the primary criteria for a destination resort: a nice weather location. Had they put the park in Spain, it probably would have been a phenomenal success.

The fourth step in making a business run well is to assess your capabilities versus those of competition. Evaluate your company and your competitors on the top two or three criteria. Know whether you have an advantage. If you are going to sell your service, you have to be able to look your customer in the eye and tell him without a shadow of a doubt, "We are better at these three items which are the most important to you."

When was the last time you asked your top four or five customers why they do business with you? Ask them what's most important about why they choose you, and how you perform when compared to your competition.

It's absolutely critical. You have to know where you stand. You have to know where you have an advantage and you have to know where you are at a disadvantage.

I go through this all before we talk about numbers because if you don't have a fundamental basis for being in a business, don't go there. It's going to be a disaster. Or, if you're looking at expanding your business, make sure you have a sound competitive advantage. All of this is market research. When I was a financial analyst, I spent more time on market research than anyone else.

If you're a small business, you can do it yourself. I canvassed my top 20 clients last week while I was putting my business plan together for next year. I asked them why they do business with me, what I do better than the competition and what I can do better for them.

You must assemble a team to succeed. You're going to have to put a financial plan together, but you need help. Doctors, lawyers and other professionals may lack basic financial skills they need to run their own business. You might be a rocket scientist and have a great product and a real niche, but you need to assemble a team early. The people you will need to include: a good accountant, a good banker and a good lawyer. I add someone to do the payroll.

Get these people on your team early. Ask them if they have experience in your industry. If they do, they are going to add value other than just getting your tax return done. They can tell you if, for example, you ought to plan on having a little more inventory, because in their experience in your industry, this is the average level. They can help you with issues you might not otherwise be aware of.

When you develop the financial plan, of course you look at your sales, your costs and your net profits. That's what motivates all of us to get into business—the net profit. "Look how I can grow that and make a ton of money."

The problem isn't the income, it's the cash flow that isn't generated. I focus a lot of my effort to help people understand the difference.

For cash flow, you start with the net income. The first thing you subtract is any additions to accounts receivable. Do you know why? Say you're a consultant. You have a great client, you've been out working hard for three months doing a great job, but now the client doesn't pay his bill.

What do you do? You have no cash flow! You have your expenses, but if you're not collecting your bills, you have nothing. You booked a nice profit and you know how much you should be making, but you're stuck. One option is to require a substantial retainer up front.

Another problem is endemic to retail: additions to inventory. Everyone underestimates the business's inventory needs.

These two elements kill small businesses: accounts receivable and additions to inventory.

Make sure you have help collecting the bills if you need it and watch the inventory levels. Once you project this for two, three or five years, you have to figure out the maximum drawdown: your worst financial scenario. If business goes out as you expect it to, but you don't collect your bills, you have to have the inventory to survive. This is where a banker and an accountant can help you.

Then, with your banker, develop a sources-and-uses statement. If you need $3 million three years from now, figure out how you are going to fund that. You don't want to end up stretched out on a personal line of credit three times your net worth. That happened to my college roommate because his single largest client defaulted.

You don't want to negotiate for more money down the road. You have to monitor and adjust the plan. Beware of fatal flaws. If 80 percent of your business is based on one client, what are you going to do if that client fails?

The last step is re-investing for growth. Every business should plan on reinvesting 10 to 15 percent of its net proceeds in the business. Use this to enhance your current products and services or develop new products and services, but be careful not to overextend. Remember to communicate your level of re-investment to existing clients and new prospects.

Don't assume those net income projections are going to flow into your bottom line. If there was only one financial report you needed to study on a regular basis, it would be your cash flow report.

Chapter 8

INTERVIEWING AND HIRING SKILLS

As you become more successful, you need to hire more people. Those people become a part of your daily life. Yet many business owners spend very little time interviewing and hiring. It's amazing.

Hiring is one of the toughest decisions you make. Those you hire are the people who represent you to the public.

Let's look at a restaurant. Usually the chef/owner is back in the kitchen supervising the quality of the food. Who encounters the customer? Generally it's the lowest paid individuals in the organization. How can you be sure that the people who represent you—the waiter in the restaurant, the receptionist in a medical or legal practice—are generating good will and providing the service you are paying them to provide?

Training is part of it. But before you train someone, you have to hire them.

Most people spend just an hour or two in an interview to choose someone they are going to spend the next five or 10 years with—virtually every day of their lives during that time.

Without formal training or preparation for interviewing, many business owners hire based on a gut feeling. Some tend to hire in their own image—they want to hire someone who is just like them. So they sit down in an interview that lacks a formal structure and they ask a couple of questions. They spend a lot of time talking about why their company is a great place to work.

Why is that?

They want the person to want the job. So instead of really qualifying that person, they spend a lot of time selling that person on wanting to come to work for them.

Now you've hired someone. Are you sure this person is competent to do the job? Are you sure this person has the kind of personality that will fit into the culture of your organization? Does this person have the kind of background and experience that will be an asset to your company?

By acting on your gut feeling, without training or preparation to interview and hire, are you hiring someone who will have to be trained completely? Are you hiring someone in whom you will have to invest many, many hours of your good time in order to give him the skills he will need to do the job?

Most interviewers are not skilled in the process of interviewing. Three very specific areas to that must be covered: competency, experience and personality.

Let's start with competency. Every job in your organization should have a list of required skills. If someone is going to be typing correspondence, certainly you would hope that person could type with a reasonable amount of speed and accuracy. It would make sense to identify such a skill. If someone is going to be greeting customers or patients on the phone, hopefully they have the skills for telephone communication. If a nurse or physician's assistant is going to do history and physicals, he should come into your organization with that competency.

Let's take the position you might hire for first—a secretary to run your business. Now what are the competencies necessary for a secretary? There is, of course, typing. What about phone personality? Can this person deal with customers in a manner that you would find appropriate? How does she handle people when they walk in? Is she capable in the areas of spelling, grammar and punctuation, and can she produce documents in a reasonable amount of time? After all, some people can spend all day typing just one letter. Does she have a sense of order? You need documents filed, organized and retrieved. Does this person have recording, documentation and filing skills?

You could probably identify 10 or 12 skills a secretary should have. Wouldn't it make sense to confirm these skills during the interview process?

What means could you take? You could set up a simulation. You could have candidates meet with people. You could have them type a report. Then they could tell you how they would organize your office and your materials.

Once you identify the competencies, you could literally spend and entire day to verify each candidate's skills. Companies that care a lot about certain jobs sometimes spend days or a week to ensure there is a good fit. It makes all the sense in the world to do that. It's like marriage and divorce: It's easy to get married and it's hard to get divorced. It's easy to hire people and it's very hard to get rid of people.

In fact, if the person you hire is from a protected class—and any individual who is not a white male under 40 is from a protected class—then your ability to terminate that person for cause becomes a much greater challenge. A small business person doesn't need an EEOC charge or a allegation of discriminatory behavior early on in the company's history.

The laws affecting employment are really not that complex. You can probably gain a working knowledge of the pertinent laws regarding employment practices in a day or so. If you're running a business, you had better be up to speed on the employment laws because if you're not, you can make terrible mistakes that will be very costly.

It's not only the legal aspect that's important, it's also good common sense. If you don't hire someone with the competence necessary to do the job that you want done, then you spend an inordinate amount of your personal time in conflict with them. "My God, I've hired the wrong people—they frustrate me, they can't type, they don't do the work the way I've instructed them. I'm very disappointed that they are not as fast as I expected. I wanted this letter done right away and eight hours later it's not done. I need them to prioritize their work…"

You can spend a lot of time frustrated with someone who might be a good person but who came to the job without the skills to do it. It happened because you failed to define those competencies and test for them in the interview.

The first step—before you hire someone—is to define the competencies you need for the job in very specific terms. You should be able to define five to seven competencies very well—if you go beyond 10 it might become a bit unwieldy. It's best to define these competencies in behavioral terms so you can evaluate the candidate.

To do this, you must walk in the shoes of the person who is going to do the job. Now it's very hard for someone who has just spent four years in medical school and five years in residency and two years in the lab to say to himself, "What does a secretary or assistant do?" If you don't know, spend some time in research. Ask a more experienced colleague about what a good secretary does and what are the important tasks and skills necessary. Better yet, ask an experienced secretary to help you define the competencies necessary to be a quality secretary.

Unless you know the skills and duties required to do the job, you cannot hire effectively. At times this job can be even more important than yours, because a front-line person can lose business for you or create more business for you. Your good work can be undone by someone who has not managed the office properly. Or it can be enhanced by a forward-thinking person who looks for ways for you to be more efficient and effective.

Take a look at billing. No matter how well you perform services, if you don't get paid, you eventually go out of business. Remember cash flow. There's a very simple business equation: Profit equals revenue minus expenses. If revenue minus expenses equals profit, you stay in business. If revenue minus expenses equals loss, you go out of business.

You have to have someone who can assure your revenue stream by:

- Making sure every single service you provide has been billed for.

- Managing your accounts receivable to make sure every single bill you send out gets paid.

- Helping you control expenses so the revenue number is higher than the expense number.

When most business owners first realize they need an office manger or a secretary to help them run the business, they think, "Gee, my wife has a friend at the gym whose sister is a secretary looking for a job. Let me interview her." She walks in the door; she looks reasonable; she seems like a nice person, and the business owner thinks, "I don't know what I really need, so why don't I avoid the hassle and just hire her."

Now the business owner has made a commitment—a commitment based on very little, if any, verification. Even worse, if he has to get rid of this person, he jeopardizes personal relationships.

Wouldn't it be better to sit down for a few hours and think about the tasks necessary to do the job and define the competencies for those tasks? Wouldn't it be better to spend a few moments on the phone with a mentor who has an office manger or a secretary asking questions such as:

- What's important about the job?

- What do you look for in a high quality secretary or

office manager?

- What does that person do that makes your job better or worse?

- What would you look for in someone to fill that position?

Wouldn't it be more effective for you, as a young professional, to spend as much time identifying what you are looking for as you spend interviewing people? It's a very important process.

Once you have come up with your list of competencies, you want to link the candidate's experience to these competencies in the interview. Does the candidate's experience demonstrate those competencies? How you ask questions of the potential employee determines whether you get the information you need.

The defined competencies should be linked to two or three open-ended questions. These questions will link the person's experience to those competencies.

The first competency we talked about was the ability to organize work and to type effectively with good grammar, spelling and punctuation.

I could come up with open-ended probes, perhaps framing the question this way: "One of the things that's very important in this practice is your ability to be organized, and to organize your work and the office. Tell me about a job experience where you used good organizational skills to be successful."

Now you've asked a very open-ended question. What do you do? You shut up and listen. Maybe you even take notes. Hopefully the person will tell you a very detailed story: "In the five years I spent at Dr.

Brown's office, I found the office was in disarray. There was nothing in place. Everything was haphazard. So I organized the place physically and then I had to organize all the files so we could get to the information. Then I organized the billing system because it was very important to make sure he billed on time. Then I organized the accounts receivable system. I even discovered services that weren't being billed properly— I discovered lost revenue."

If someone gives such a specific answer to an open-ended question, you have evidence that you can verify. This person's experience seems to demonstrate competence in the area you have asked about.

You might also reverse the question: "Tell me about a time in your work experience when you were not organized." You want to get the other side, too. Everyone has had problems.

In response to another question, the person might describe something that demonstrates honesty. When you are listening to these stories, you are hearing things about the person's credibility, personality and experience. These are indicators of how the candidate's relationship with you might or might not work.

What if the candidate, says, "Well, I had one job with Dr. White. He was so disorganized and so frustrating. I tried to organize that office and he would just mess it up. I couldn't deal with him at all."

Alarms should go off now. You are starting to see something about this person. Yes, she is very organized, but she also may be very controlling. If you can't adapt to someone trying to control your organizational behavior, you are going to have a clash at some point. If you want to sit back and let someone else create the organizational structure of your office, this might be an ideal candidate. If you want to be involved in the organizational structure, this person might not be the best for you.

In the interview, you are asking a series of open-ended probes designed to get the person to tell you about his competencies and experience.

You also want to be very clear on how you define these competencies. For example, "Trust is very important to the running of the business. Everyone in the organization has a key to the office. Everyone has access to the computer and the files. Tell me how, in your work life, you have experienced the issue of trust," or, "Tell me about an experience where trust was lacking and how that affected your job performance."

You will get some enlightening answers to these probes. The more complex the position, the more careful you have to be in defining the competencies and then verifying them through the interview process.

Let's upgrade this a bit. You've done a good job as a doctor, lawyer or small business person hiring office staff. Your business is very successful. Now you have to hire a colleague to cover some of the workload.

For physicians, hiring is often based on references from peers, especially people with whom they studied. It's easy to become bogged down with someone's CV. I've seen CVs that are so thick you can measure them with a ruler. It's very easy to forget about the competence issue when the CV shows a list of impressive articles and that the candidate studied under a professor that you respect.

However, when you run a business, you hire people to do the work you don't like to do so you can do more of the work that you enjoy. If you can't figure this out, you should be working for someone else—not running your own business.

You are going to hire a colleague, perhaps someone to be your second—someone who will represent you to your other colleagues and your patients. This person is going to be as much your representative as you are. It becomes even more critical in this situation that you define the competencies necessary to do the job. You must use the interview process to determine that past experience demonstrates the competency to do the job as you have designed it.

This leads me to the third area of good hiring practice: personality. We all create a culture—within our family and our business. A culture for a small company probably represents the personality of the founder and the head of the company. That culture might be fast-paced and energetic, it might be laid-back and reserved. That culture might be focused primarily on the customer or on the operating procedures and policies of the organization.

A company culture, which also affects the informal way policies are enforced, is as important to success as the volume of business. In fact, these components are inextricably bound. People do well when their personalities and the company culture are aligned. Someone who is energetic and fast-paced does much better in an organization that is energetic and fast-paced. Aggressive people tend to be overbearing in the operation of a laid-back company. And a laid-back person in an aggressive culture will never get up to speed.

When there is not a proper fit, the business owner and the employee get frustrated. Again, it's very important to define terms: Just what is the culture of the company? A lot of it goes back to the mission we defined in the chapter on strategic planning. What are you going to achieve? And what will people think and feel and see when they walk into your office? Are they going to see a highly efficient operation that is customer focused, or are they going to see an operation that is focused on what happens behind the windows?

It always amazes me when I am in someone's office and that person takes a phone call. He spends time with the individual on the phone, yet I'm there in person and he's putting me off. Whether it's a retail establishment or a professional practice, how can the person on the phone be the priority over the person who is in front of you? This has always befuddled me.

Is that the culture of the company? Is it primarily a telephone operation? Or could it be this company has no culture when it comes to relating to customers? Do people really matter when they come to the office?

The culture of a company will represent who they really are. If you walk into an office and you see piles of paper on the desk and boxes in the corner, are you going to think of it as an organized company? Or are you going to see it as being in disarray? If you're an organized person, are you going to be able to work in this company?

Many employers will determine the type of person they are looking for, which to some extent comes down to personality. They may be looking for an aggressive, self-starter—someone who can get the job done on her own and doesn't need a lot of supervision. They may be looking for someone who works hard and plays hard, someone who is dedicated to her job and her company. Is this an indication of the company's culture?

If you've done a good job of defining your culture, how do you ensure that the candidate has the qualities you want? You tell him, and then ask him about his traits. For example: "Joe, I don't believe in a lot of supervising of people. I believe people in my organization will find the work that needs to get done and then get it done without me having to tell them what to do. I need someone who will create work, create opportunity and complete the mission. Tell me about your past experience and how you've worked in such environments. What was good about it? What was frustrating about it? What do you look for in a boss?"

The candidate might be looking for a boss who is 500 miles away and will let him do what he wants within the parameters of the goal. Such a candidate would be very unhappy in an organization with a boss who is next to him and wants to see every bit of his productivity.

If we go back and examine our past, I think we find we had jobs that were really terrific. We can't always define why they were great—it wasn't necessarily the pay or the hours or the benefits—we just enjoyed getting up and going to work.

I worked for 12 years after college before I found a company whose culture fit my personality.

I remember being told by several employers that they saw me as a diamond in the rough; if they could just polish me up I could be really valuable for them. What they were really saying was that I didn't fit in with the company. I had good qualities and behaviors and traits that they were happy with, but I just didn't fit the culture. I didn't look how they wanted me to look; I didn't act how they wanted me to act. No matter how much polishing they did, I would never fit into their company.

So many people fail to understand the element of aligning personality to the corporate culture. A person can wonder for years and years why she can't seem to move ahead in an organization. She's not happy with the job and she can't seem to please anyone. Very often it's not her job performance that is the problem, it's that her personality and the culture of the company are not aligned.

Unfortunately, the owners of most companies don't define their culture for others. They might be afraid to; they don't want their milieu represented to the public. But it always comes out anyway. You can't hide the culture of a company from the public. At some point, if the company is successful, people are going to be interested to find out what makes it tick.

For example, some companies have a command and control or a power culture. One or two or three executives at the top make the majority of the decisions. If you're a person who likes a lot of authority and likes to make a lot of decisions and you're in a middle-management role, then you will not want to be a part of a command-and-control cultured company because you are not going to make decisions. You are going to make recommendations; other people are going to make decisions.

If you want to make a lot of decisions as a middle manager, you want to be in a company whose culture is much more about accountability—where authority is delegated. You want a company that allows middle management to become involved in decision making.

I worked for a company for years where the CEO was involved in decisions that many thought were quite beneath his position. But that's how he chose to run his business. He wanted to be involved with all types of decisions. He wanted to ensure the quality of work was at a certain level of perfection. His opinion of how to do that was to get involved in projects early on, set direction and assign responsibilities. Many people who came to that company wanting to make high-level decisions left frustrated. They were never going to be able do that at that company. Conversely, those people whose personality fit that culture—people who didn't care whether they made big decisions—did very well. They made recommendations and tried to sell the boss. They had long, happy and prosperous careers with the company.

That company also was driven by a high work ethic. Most of the people who succeeded saw their work as the most important thing in their lives and were willing to work long, hard hours to succeed. Additionally, the environment was intense and driven. If work was important to you and you were intense and driven, willing to do what it took to get the job done, it was a great place to work. If you were more concerned with your job description or time off, and if you felt uncomfortable in a high pressure situation, it was a terrible place to work. These are the types of problems on jobs that don't come from mismanagement or incompetence: They come from bad fits between an individual's personality and a company's culture.

Cultures and personalities can both be described with action terms: driven, intense, self-starting, accountable, no-excuse, role-oriented, power, collaborative, team-like, competitive, laid-back, customer-focused, policy-and-procedure-focused, rule-oriented, or outcome-oriented. It is important to define the culture of your organization and try to let people know what it is during the interview process. Then you and they can be sure the culture of your organization fits their personality.

In hiring, do you really want to spend just an hour or two before you make a lifelong commitment? Wouldn't it be beneficial for everyone to spend time:

- Defining the competencies necessary to do the job. Structure an interview so that you can ask the kinds of questions that will demonstrate the person's experience in terms of the job competencies.

- Defining your corporate culture. Ask specific questions of the candidate about aspects of his personality and how that fits your company's culture.

- Looking for a person's experience that fits the competency needed for the job and shows that his personality aligns with the corporate culture.

Experience doing the job you want them to do is critical. If I am running an academic practice that relies on research grants, then I want to hire a junior colleague who has experience obtaining grants. Conversely, if I have a private practice that requires a high patient load, I won't care about a junior colleague's research experience. Make sure the person's successful experience corresponds to the job you want him to perform.

Let's talk about the process of the interview. Many business people begin with the idea, "I want to like the person who walks in the door. I want to get it over with. I don't want to interview 10 or 15 people."

Begin the interview process in that state of mind and you are already in trouble. You are absolutely irrational. You're acting on impulse.

It's important to have a structure for your interview that allows you to see the good things but also look for the bad things. The long view is that the person might be with you for the rest of your career. This might be a very hard person to get rid of for reasons other than incompetence. There might be other factors, having nothing to do with cause, that make this person difficult to work with.

All of this information is available to you during the interview if you only take the time to look for it. Get a second opinion from peers and/or subordinates. This feedback is invaluable, filling in your blind spots and showing you how the candidate treats people.

When I conduct an interview, I like to look at the resume in advance and develop specific questions related to background and experience. Then I can spend my time during the interview listening rather than scrambling for my next question. I like to start out with five minutes of chit-chat. I want to find out a little bit about the person's "non-work" personality. Can she hold a conversation? How does she conduct herself?

Then I tell the candidate how the interview will unfold: "Jane, we're going to take about an hour, hour and a half to conduct this interview. The first third will be me asking specific questions about your background and experience, and I'll actually listen to your responses. For the second third we will turn it around: I'll let you ask me any questions you want to about the job, the business, the company, whatever you come up with. The last third will be both of us deciding whether we want to continue with this process."

Here are some sample questions:

- Tell me about the best job you ever had and why that was the case?

• Tell me about the best boss you ever had. What were the qualities that impressed you?

• Tell me what you didn't like about past jobs.

• The responsibilities of the job require a high level of customer contact. Tell me about your past experiences where your customer contact resulted in improved performance for your company.

• Our culture is fast-paced and based on individual accountability. Tell me about past job experiences where you did well in this type of environment. Also, tell me about times where this caused you problems.

• This job requires accurate reports and billing information to be delivered on a timely basis. Tell me how in your past jobs you have been able to provide accurate, timely reports without a lot of supervision.

During the interview, I'm going to take some notes so I can review them later. If I'm talking to six or seven people over a period of several days it's hard to separate who said what. They begin to run together.

What am I looking for when the candidate asks me questions? I want some indication that the candidate has done some homework on the company or the practice; that she's not coming in ice cold. If she hasn't done any research, there's a problem.

I want to make sure the candidate is asking good questions. If she asks whether getting to work on time is important, I'm going to say "yes." If she asks the times when it's necessary to come in early and the times when it doesn't matter, then I'm going to give a much more in-depth answer. I might say, "Jane, if we have a deadline, if we're in a tight squeeze to get something done, then I need you to be here on time and early would be even better. If there's no pressing deadline, I'm honestly not concerned about the precise time you arrive as long as you fulfill all commitments and get the job done." Now you can only give that last answer if it's true.

I'm also looking at how the candidate tries to get information from me to make a decision. This gives me an indication of intelligence and a demonstration of logic.

The hard part is the final third of the interview. I might ask, if things are going well, "Is this a job you still would be interested in?" If the answer is affirmative, I will ask, "Why?"

Now I want the candidate to reconfirm interest. In the next step I will take some time to close the sale. After all, we are both making decisions.

I might say, "Jane, I think this will be a great job for you. Your background and experience match the opportunity perfectly. The culture of our company is one in which you will feel comfortable. I think you will like the freedom I provide to explore and develop your skills. This will help fulfill your needs and the needs of the company. You are the kind of person that will help make this company great."

If I'm not sure, I'm going to go back and ask more questions. "Tell me again about..."

Interviewing boils down to simple steps. If you want to hire the right person, you have to do your homework. You have to do a challenging interview.

You have to challenge your gut feeling because your gut feeling is going to want to hire the first person who walks through the door.

Once the interview is over and you make a decision, never give the person an answer while she is sitting there. I might say, "I think you're a highly-qualified candidate, but I'm interviewing some other people. I'll be back to you within several days to let you know if the job is yours." Whether the candidate is good or bad, give the same answer. If I really like the candidate, then I am going to give her a positive indication like, "Jane, I think this is a great fit for both of us, but I still need to check your references, I'll do that quickly and get back to you with an answer by Friday. How does that sound to you?"

If I don't want to hire the candidate, I will tell her I will get back to her in a couple of days. Why not just tell the person on the spot? I don't want to sit there and debate why I'm not going to give her the job. Frankly, I'm not there to help her interview in the future.

Give yourself some time. Look at all the candidates. Check references. Check every bit of information you can.

Even if you work hard at interviewing, you still can make mistakes, but the harder you work at finding the right employees, the better opportunity you and your organization will have to succeed.

No matter how big your organization, interviewing and hiring are critical to your success. In fact, the smaller your organization, the more critical those first few hires are to your short-term success. Remember long-term success starts with short-term success. Think long-term and work harder short-term and you will succeed in building an organization that will help you succeed.

Epilogue

Now that you have been exposed to the concepts of these practical business skills, you might want to apply some of these to your organization or your practice. Like any new skills, just reading about them is helpful, but if you want to put them into practice, it will take effort and initiative. In fact, it will take 28 days of practice to make any new skill a habit. Also, the first time you change your behavior with your co-workers and subordinates, they will be suspicious even if they like the new way you are behaving. Let them in on your plan. Ask them to support the changes you are trying to make in both your behavior and the working environment of your organization.

You may need some additional information to make the appropriate changes in your behavior. That information is available in a variety of books available on the open market. Also, there are many organizational consultants who conduct seminars on many of the topics available in this book.

Charles Johnson

Some of the books we recommend:

• *The One Minute Manager* by Ken Blanchard and Spencer Johnson

• *Leadership and the One Minute Manager* by Ken Blanchard, Patricia Zigarmi, and Drea Zigarmi

• *Seven Habits of Highly Effective People* by Steven Covey

• *Getting to Yes: Negotiating Agreement Without Giving In* by Roger Fisher

• *Kilmann Conflict Mode Questionnaire* by Kenneth Thomas and Ralph Kilmann

• *Getting Hired!: Winning Strategies to Ace the Interview* by Paul C. Green

Charles Johnson's firm, Medical Education Training Associates of Connecticut, helps doctors, bankers and other professionals run their businesses. Johnson's lectures and training sessions are in high demand nationally. He began his career as a high school teacher and went on to become Vice President of Education & Training for United States Surgical Corporation.

Andy Thibault, is an award-winning columnist for *The Connecticut Law Tribune* and veteran investigative reporter and feature writer. Thibault's work appears in many publications including *Connecticut Magazine* and *Northeast Magazine*. He manages an endowment that awards $19,000 annually to teenage writers, the IMPAC Connecticut State University Young Writers Awards. He also edits an international business newsletter, *APS Quarterly*.

ORDER FORM

Michelle Publishing Company
2275 Silas Deane Highway
Rocky Hill, CT 06067
860-721-8800 (Office) 860-721-1694 (Fax)

Number of Copies	Price per Copy
1	$12.00
2-5	11.00
5-9	10.00
10-99	9.00
100 and over	8.00

Please send me _____ copies of *The 12-Minute MBA for Doctors*. Please include $2.00 for postage and handling for one book and 50 cents for each additional book, not to exceed $12.00. Prices subject to change without notice. Add 25% for Canada. Do not send cash.

Name_____

Address_____

City_____ State/Zip_____

___ Check Enc   ___Visa   ___MC

Card # _____ Exp. Date_____

Signature_____